"This Is A Golf Club"

It's never too late for a first lesson...

Dr. Terry Zachary
Golf • Health • Life

Library and Archives Canada Cataloguing in Publication

Zachary, Terry, 1964-
      This is a golf club : it's never too late for a first lesson / Terry Zachary.

ISBN 0-9739638-0-8

      1. Golf--Fiction. I. Title.

PS8649.A27T44 2005   **C813'.6**   **C2005-907641-0**

Comments, Testimonials & Bulk Purchase Information:
This Is A Golf Club
1124 Fir Ave #114
Blaine, WA
USA 98230
www.thisisagolfclub.com

Printed and bound in Canada by
First Choice Books
2-460 Tennyson Place
Victoria BC V8Z 6S8
Ph:(250)383-6353
www.firstchoicebooks.ca

The story to follow does not claim to and is not intended to replace professional golf, psychological and/or health advice, action, opinion or diagnosis.

For Mom, Darryl, Jo & the Munchkins.

Before You Begin...

A few notes before you begin this unique golf journey:

Inside you will notice that all golf references are to a right-handed golfer. Current and future lefties, here is your apology in advance: *Sorry*. Substitute *left* for *right* and *right* for *left* in all golf *handedness* situations. Maybe you are used to this adjustment already, maybe not—*Sorry* just the same.

The story is set in a small Canadian city. Occasional language references and spellings are Canadian-specific. For example, you will notice: "colour" instead of "color" and "fibre" instead of "fiber." These references are designed to be educational for readers around the world. You will pick up interesting spellings that are specific to this wonderful country.

There will follow regular references to the golf teachers of Canada, the members of the CPGA (Canadian Professional Golf Association). Please substitute the PGA membership of your respective country. PGA members around the world have shown quiet leadership, bringing the game of golf from obscurity to its current position of prominence in world popularity. They are the unsung heroes of the game and deserve the praise of all golfers. *Thank you for your hard work and dedication. Keep it up.*

To find links and information on references within the story, check the website www.thisisagolfclub.com; or email info@thisisagolfclub.com with your questions, testimonials and/or comments or for bulk purchase information, or write to the address listed at the beginning of the book.

The story to follow does not claim to or is not meant to replace professional golf, psychological and/or health advice, action, opinion or diagnosis. It certainly *is* designed to stimulate thought, study and progress.

To my current and former golf colleagues: Most all of you have played a part in this book. The experiences that I have had as a professional golfer—both in being beaten badly and in performing to a high level—have been deeply enlightening. I am blessed to have lived inside this fascinating, frustrating and tough world.

To my former patients: If I have made near the difference in your lives that you have in mine, well then *the world is working.* You have taught me as much as I could ever have taught you.

To corporate golf in Canada, USA, and Mexico: Quite simply: Invest in the Canadian Professional Golf Tour. It is the most talent-heavy tour (per investment dollar) to be found in the world today. To inquire, call: 1-877-CAN-TOUR (226-8687).

Additional thanks to my editor Dawn–Louis McLeod, to CPGA professionals Phillip Jonas, Troy Peverly, Tom Whittle and Mark Kuhn, to professional players Darren Griff (Asian Tour) and Kent Fukishima (Canadian Tour) and to business-people and friends Kirk Fisher (Lark Group, Surrey, Canada), Anne & Art Fawcett (Ridge Meadow Farms, Langley, Canada), Joanne McLennan (McLennan Window Fashions, Langley, Canada) and Shellee Neinau.

My final thank you's go to various supporters along the way who said, "You can" and also to various *motivators* who said, "You can't." Both have played a great role in the making of this book. I am convinced more than ever that any accomplishment of value requires purpose, sacrifice, hard work and faith—and some degree of risk. Follow your heart. My most honest life interests have led me here.

Enjoy,

Dr. Terry Zachary

Table of Contents

Chapter 1

A Young Champion

The sun was low and the shadows long at the Connaught *Golf Club* in Medicine Hat, Alberta, Canada. There beside the 18*th* green stood a sunburnt sixteen-year-old local golfer named Billy Black. Hunched on his putter, left foot over right, Billy had a five-shot lead.

Billy's nearest challenger was seventeen-year-old Kip Koning of nearby Lethbridge. Kip methodically lined up a four-foot par putt, his mannerisms reflecting imminent defeat.

Billy knew that Kip must be disappointed. Each had hoped to win in Medicine Hat to gain additional scholarship attention from U.S. college recruiters. Billy was the number one ranked junior golfer in southern Alberta—Kip was number two. They were good friends. U.S. golf schools had been recruiting both for years now. Unfortunately for Kip, the story of this tournament was about to write its own ending—another Billy Black win. And why not? Billy had proved himself by far the best player this week.

Billy had come to relish this time—late afternoon on the final day of a golf tournament. It usually meant he's right in the thick of competition. It usually meant another tournament win. It seemed as if wins were coming more easily these days for Billy. It seemed as if the sky were the limit.

Billy's ball marker lay a foot from the final hole. He waited to ceremoniously tap in for par—and for his third straight Southeastern Alberta Junior Golf Championship.

His calm, stoic pose, however, was misleading. His thoughts were running wildly inside his head: How many under par was he today—two or three? How big was his lead—five or six? What a great weekend it had been. And he's only sixteen years old. He'll be eligible to play in this tournament two more times. Could he win five in a row? Maybe he'll play NCAA Division I golf in the States. This convincing win will look good to recruiters. Maybe he'll play on the PGA Tour someday! What great feats he'll accomplish in this game—his game. Time is on his side.

Billy gazed at the small crowd that had gathered around the 18th green. Side by side were his mom, Megan, his dad, Randy, his older brother Danny and Billy's girlfriend, Leah. His mom and dad, both golf fanatics, wore sunglasses and golf hats. Everyone beamed as they watched the finish. Danny was like a rock, save for the hint of a proud smirk. Leah looked like a dream—slim, tall, tanned and beautiful. She was smiling directly at Billy. Their eyes met for a moment—a special moment. Billy returned a quick smile, but was careful to spare the tender feelings of his "victims" with what might appear as "rubbing it in".

He noticed others in the crowd, including his high school gym teacher Jim Bloom, his club pro Gus Geraldi, various friends, fellow golfers, and local sports reporter Ted Sillinger. This was a big deal. This was Billy Black's moment.

"Billy? Are you with us?" Dad whispers as he nudges me with his elbow. "We're all here for you, Bud. It'd be nice if you'd join us."

I sit up at attention. Dad, Gus Geraldi, club pro here at the Medicine Hat Country Club, and Lou Ogilvie, club president, have been discussing my future. And, as I have a tendency to do, I have been daydreaming.

"Ah—yeah, Dad—sure—Sorry—where were we?"

"Like I said, Ben Farr has agreed to meet with us," grumbles Gus. "If he takes you on, Billy, you'll have to get over to the Connaught Club by 3:30 on Tuesdays and Fridays. Is that a problem?"

The Connaught Golf Club is on the other side of Medicine Hat, or "The Hat" as we locals affectionately call our city. It's the other golf course in town. And Ben Farr is the head club pro there.

"No problem," I say excitedly. "I can get there by 3:30 easy."

Gus nods and proceeds to discuss scheduling issues with my Dad and Lou.

It's a Sunday afternoon in early April. For four years running, Dad and I have met with Gus and Lou to discuss my summer tournament schedule and expenses.

You see, each year the Medicine Hat Golf and Country Club sends its junior club champion to the provincial and national junior golf championships, all expenses paid. It's the club's way of developing participation in and promoting junior golf. And it works. Our club's junior golf program is one of the strongest in all of southern Alberta. As I said, for four years running, yours truly has been the program's benefactor.

This year's meeting is different though. Ben Farr will be joining us at 4 pm. Recently Gus spoke about me to Ben, who I assume is well aware of my credentials. By now, every golfer in the Hat recognizes my potential to move forward in the game. Much has been written in the local newspaper about my accomplishments. I know I can raise my game to another level, but not by myself. I need a coach and a mentor who can give me feedback and direction. Until now, my only golf instruction has come from my Dad and from Gus' junior program—hardly what's considered advanced training for a player of my calibre.

I'm well aware of Ben's credentials. He came close to winning the Canadian Amateur Golf Championship a few times, played various professional mini-tours around the world and eventually became a regular on the Canadian Professional Golf Tour. He played a bit on the Asian Tour and even played a dozen or so Buy.com (now Nationwide) and a few PGA Tour events. As golf goes in southern Alberta, he's the man. I've wanted his help for some time now, but have never been able to ask. Until now, I wasn't sure I deserved his attention. But now, coming off the best season of any Hat junior golfer ever, I feel I've earned the right to at least ask.

"If Ben decides to take you on, Billy, you'll get one chance only," Gus addresses me. "He's a no nonsense guy—he knows what it takes to be competitive in this game—I see how committed you are, Billy, but—I'm just saying—are you sure this is what you want?" Gus hesitates. "More people are taking a stake in you. That can be a lot to handle for a kid your age."

"I'm sure, Gus," I say, nodding like gunfire at our heavyset pro. "I've been sure for a long time."

"Randy—Billy has your support in this?" Gus hoists his brow towards Dad.

"Of course," Dad nods.

"All right then."

Everyone's attention shifts to the adjacent west window. Our once virile golf course lies barren and brown, gaunt like a healed wrist fracture newly out of its cast. But to a Canadian golfer, this is the wonderful guise of the new season, the transformation from winter to spring. The trees are leafless and the grass colourless, yet a sense of soon-to-be vitality trumps it all.

In the distance, a black rectangle vibrates toward the clubhouse. Everyone at the table recognizes Ben Farr's vehicle.

Instantly, my stomach knots up. This is it. Will Ben really be interested in helping me? How much will he want to change my game? Will his help hurt my short-term tournament chances? I've heard stories of PGA pros struggling to make cuts after changing their swing. Now more than ever I need to win. I need to continue to feed tournament statistics to U.S. college recruiters. Of all years, this is the year that will make or break me in choosing a good U.S. school. Or will Ben Farr just laugh at me for making such a big deal of myself?

With 5 minutes to spare, Ben walks from the parking lot to the clubhouse. He moves with a noticeable ease of motion and balance. He enters and pauses briefly before spotting our group.

Unlike Gus, Ben is an athletic looking man—tall, dark and wiry—with an unmistakable presence—he resonates success with every motion. His face is long, thin and triangular. His hair is black and neat. I have always admired Ben's well-dressed and professional appearance. He looks like a tour pro. Ben Farr is my idol.

Ten years ago I watched Ben play in the Calgary Open, a Canadian Professional Tour event. He shot 65 on the tough Heritage Point Golf Course—and made it look like a walk in the park. Watching that round inspired me to become a professional golfer as much as any round I have ever seen. It was real—and I was there. The sounds that day were raw and intense, different than on TV. That day made playing golf for a living seem possible.

I replay Ben's immaculate golf swing in my mind. I see in him what I want for myself. Now he's about to sit with me and show an interest in my career.

"Good afternoon gentlemen—Billy—Randy—Gus—Lou." He shakes each of our hands maintaining eye contact, as if each were the only man in the room. I manage a pleasant smile. It's the first time he's ever spoken to me. My body is shaking. "Hi Ben" is all I can come up with.

The rest of the group exchanges pleasantries and idle chitchat. Ben sits to my left, his posture upright, yet relaxed. He even smells successful. Dad is sitting to my right. Strangely, I have never felt so comfortable in all my life.

The two head professionals settle in, briefly discussing preparations for the upcoming golf season. Though friendly, the two are not close. And they couldn't be more opposite. Ben is a *golfer's* golf pro. Gus is more a *friend* of the membership, more a pro-shop manager. They *do* appear to agree on one thing, though—my golf career is worthy of discussion.

At last, Gus breaks the ice. The meeting *proper* is on.

"Ben, as you know, I've asked you here today on behalf of Billy and Randy." He clears his throat. "I've helped Billy along about as much as I know how to. Randy, of course, has had a great influence on his son's game as well. That said, we both feel his game has advanced beyond where either of us can be effective. The time has come for Billy to crank up his golf education. He needs an advanced coach." Gus takes a quick slurp of his coffee, as Ben's expression reads "straight flush". "I've never asked anything of you before, Ben. Then again, I've never had a golfer of Billy's calibre before. You must be aware of his success last year. Ben—what I'm trying to say is—rather, what I'm trying to ask is—will you be Billy's coach?"

So awkward is Gus' manner that it clouds his request. Still, the issue is on the table. Silence forces all eyes over to Ben.

Ben Farr gazes away quietly for a moment, then adjusts his body to address Dad and I directly. His voice is calm. "Billy, the most important instruction I ever received came well after my playing days. I've often wondered what my life would have been like had I received this instruction earlier. There is so much for you to learn now before ever considering to work with me—or any teacher for that matter. It is also why I must decline your flattering request."

Everyone listening freezes as Ben's comments sink in.

What did he say? What just happened? I feel tears welling up. I've prepared myself for every possible outcome—except this one! My boyhood idol has just turned me down flat! And with virtually no emotion—in fact, with a smile on his face!

Ben seems to recognize the shock in the eyes of the meeting participants. Matter-of-factly, he re-addresses his stunned table partners. "There's no sense in Billy driving all of the way across town to see me now when the person he most needs to speak with is right here at your club. He'll know who you are. He follows the local golf scene. Walk out to the driving range and talk to him. He's out there most evenings."

"*Tom Morrison?*" Gus barks. "Are you nuts, Ben? You can't be serious!"

"I'm not nuts and I've never been more serious."

"He's no coach, Ben—he's a range picker!" Gus rants. "He's a bit 'out there,' too. I've nearly fired him a dozen times. I would have, but the seniors would kill me. They love him—he gives them free golf tips. Ol' buggers would never pay for lessons anyway, so I don't care. He can share his abstract thoughts with them, but not with Billy. I don't want him in Billy's head. I cannot agree to this."

Ben's posture and facial expression remain unchanged. "Tom will teach Billy more in a few weeks than I could in a lifetime. If Billy spends time with Tom, he'll better comprehend what any future teacher offers him, about anything—golf included."

Gus counters. "Morrison won't say two words to me about golf. I don't know what to make of him. I don't think he knows anything about modern golf principles anyway, like mental approach—exercise—equipment—nothing! He never talks to me about the meat-and-potatoes of the golf swing, and frankly, I don't think he can! I think he worries about embarrassing himself. I've heard he could play in his day, but that's a long time ago. And he's no teacher. He's outdated, Ben. Billy needs a modern teacher. Morrison talks about history and nature and grandchildren. That's all I ever hear about. I don't get it."

Ben has listened to every word and replies calmly. "He doesn't talk to you, Gus, because you are not in need of his words. You teach golf lessons and run your pro-shop and probably seem quite content to him to do so. But you never have, nor will ever have, to put your words on the line. I mean really on the line—competing—risking everything—your reputation—your family's reputation—your livelihood—your well-being—your sanity. And that's okay, Gus. But Tom has. And I have. And Billy will have to in time. Tom can prepare Billy better than anyone for what's ahead of him. He's a specialist—a *guide*. That's how he puts it. He has spent most of the last twenty years in the USA, Europe and abroad, observing golf—and ways of life in general. His way is fascinating. I wish he could speak to everyone in the world, golfer or otherwise. I bet he'd work with Billy though, if Randy and Billy ask. He's too busy to chase people around."

"Too busy?" Gus snarls. "Only *if* they ask? What are you talking about Ben? He's a friggin' range picker!"

Ben remains calm. "There's more to people than what we see with our eyes, Gus. Tom showed me that. He helps people see what they can't understand and understand what they can't see."

Ben smiles as he rises from the table. "Gentlemen, I've told you much more than Tom would have ever liked. If that's all you need from me, I'll be on my way." He shakes each man's hand and then focuses his brown eyes on me. "You have my suggestion, Billy. It comes from the heart."

With that, Ben Farr turns and is gone.

Chapter 2

Randy Acts

"Wake up, Billy—wake up—I need to talk to you," Dad whispers.

Where am I? What time is it? I search for my clock. "Dad?" I mumble, barely cognitive. "It's quarter to six in the morning."

"I didn't sleep last night, Billy. I need to talk to you right now about what Ben said yesterday. I can't let you miss out on what might be a fantastic opportunity."

"You mean what he didn't say," I whine, half asleep and fully bewildered.

"He said a lot, Billy. Ben said he would teach you."

"He did not, Dad," I whisper despondently. "He said he *wouldn't* teach me. He passed me off on that crazy old range picker. I can't believe we even asked him. Ben doesn't have time for me. He's a busy—"

"That's enough, Billy!" Dad's stern whisper interrupts. "Ben said you didn't need him *now*. He said there was no point coming across town *now*. He said the man on the range could help you *now*. He was being sincere, Billy."

"It's his fancy way of saying no," I counter.

Dad is not impressed. "Billy, you've said for years that you want to play professional golf someday. You're well on your way to having a chance to try it." Dad hesitates, as if a *but* is coming. "Truth be said, success has come easily for you so far. That won't last, Billy. It's time we talk about the real world."

Dad lets out a deep sigh. I sigh too. This is a lot to hear before six in the morning.

"When I was your age, I wanted to play in the NHL more than anything in the world. I was one of the best hockey players in town. It was so easy, until junior hockey. That's when my attitude caught up to me. I ran into the best fifteen- and sixteen-year-old hockey players in the world—players who had been improving their skills every day for years. They were bigger than me, stronger, faster—and smarter. Like a punch in the face, hockey suddenly became difficult. As hard as I worked, I couldn't catch up to their skill level. I was too far behind. I hadn't looked for ways to move forward, to improve along the way. Maybe I was scared to improve at that point in my life, scared to get out of my comfort zone. I was a big fish in a small pond. Eventually, I had no choice but to give up my dream."

Dad labors and pauses. I've never seen him like this before.

"I learned a lot, Billy. I knew that I hadn't given it my best effort—not even close. I refocused and vowed never again to let my bad attitude and lack of effort hold me back in anything. I looked for every bit of information and every challenge that might help me to improve. My new-found attitude allowed me to build a successful sales career and to be a good husband and father."

I can only nod—the lump in my throat is keeping me from doing anything else.

"I won't watch the same thing happen to you, Billy," Dad continues. "I'm willing to bet you'll be just fine if you give golf your best shot."

I nod in agreement, now feeling foolish for my reaction to Ben's advice. It's not quite that simple, though. "What about what Gus said, Dad? He's helped me so much over the years." I whisper as if Gus might hear us. "He says Old Tom Morrison's crazy. I feel weird about getting help against his advice—and from his own range picker? How's Gus gonna feel?"

"That's not your problem, son." Dad's eyebrows rise. "The way I see it, Gus has very little idea of the real world of professional golf. Ben Farr does. He's been there. He's lived it." Dad's tone becomes stern. "It's time you learned to be your own person, Billy. This is a good opportunity for you to learn about taking action. Do what's right, son. It's your life, not Gus'."

I had no idea Dad was this perceptive. His advice stirs me— but I still have another concern. "What about Gus saying he didn't want Old Tom inside my head?"

Dad responds quickly. "Gus' advice seems to me to be based on fear and ignorance, Billy. Gus fears things that are different—or people that are different—or he fears failing—or fears failing you—or fears not being accepted—I can't quite put my finger on it. Either way, fear and ignorance impair progress and close many doors for many people, doors that may have lead to great opportunity. Fear and ignorance played a role in the demise of one of my dreams—don't let them affect yours." Dad hesitates and shakes his head. "Gus may mean well, but is teaching you to be afraid of making mistakes. There's no such thing as *mistakes*, Billy. Only *choices* and *outcomes* are real. Make your best choice, deal with the outcome, and move on. *'No Fear'*, that's what you kids are saying nowadays, right?"

"Right, Dad—about five years ago!" I had to *take action* to stop Dad's attempt at being *hip*!

"Go see Old Tom. You'll learn a valuable lesson—the lesson of action. I bet you'll feel good about it. I believe Ben gave you honest advice. Only when you act will you discover the true outcome." Dad softens his expression. "Remember, it's the only way Ben will work with you anyway, right? What's the worse that could happen?"

"Old Tom could be an axe murderer," I say in my best creepy voice.

We laugh in unison.

"Thanks, Dad," I say. "Can we talk to Old Tom tonight? He'll be out on the driving range."

"No time like the present," Dad grins. "I'll bring a 3-iron along in case he's got the axe with him."

"I think it should be a 2-iron—I heard he's pretty nuts!"

Again we laugh.

"Get up for breakfast," Dad says and then police dog sniffs the air. "Mom's got it started."

He turns to leave my room.

"Dad?" I quip.

He turns back.

"Do you still wish you were playing in the NHL?" I ask.

Dad chuckles. "No, Billy—I think I'm about where I'm supposed to be."

*

At 6 pm, I'm busy hitting chip shots to the practice green when Dad's car makes its way towards the golf course parking lot.

He picks me up most nights at this time on his way home from work. Danny usually drops me off here after school. This crazy schedule allows me to play or at least practice everyday after school. Tonight, Dad and I will go to the driving range and talk to Old Tom Morrison. Dinner will be delayed even more than usual.

From the practice green, I can see Old Tom on the driving range picking range balls. From what I can make of it, he collects the range balls that are too close to the fence for the motorized range ball picker to get to. Old Tom works Mondays, Wednesdays, Fridays and Saturdays from April to October, starting an hour or two before the sun goes down. I have no idea what he does in the winter.

What has he done with his life to need this job?

Dad is now walking toward me from the parking lot. He's about average height and relatively slim, save for a little belly bulge, has dark features and is balding slightly. He still has the strut of an athlete. And he's good at every sport he tries— hockey, golf, tennis, bowling, baseball, pool—every sport. He's dressed in a business suit, consistent with his insurance-selling career. He has worked his way up to be one of the best salespeople at Grant Anderson Insurance in The Hat. A pretty cool Dad, I think.

"All set, Billy?" Dad asks as he approaches, throwing his jacket over his shoulder. "Gather up your stuff and let's go talk to him."

Then it happens—another fear attack. Negative thoughts flash wildly through my mind. I feel sick to my stomach. What if he says *no*? Or what if he says *yes* and screws up my swing? Or screws up my mind? Will Ben really work with me even if I do see Old Tom Morrison? What will my friends think of me hanging out with some old range picker? What will Gus think?

"'You okay, son?" Dad's voice breaks in. "You look sick."

"I still feel weird about going to see Old Tom Morrison," I say. "I mean, what are people gonna think? And what if he screws up my swing? Or what if he screws with my mind?"

"You want to work with Ben don't you, Billy?" Dad says, with all of the sternness from this morning.

I nod *yes*.

"Then I suggest you pull it together. You'll have much tougher things to do in your life than this. Enjoy the experience of taking action, kiddo. Remember, *choices* and *outcomes* only." Dad's tone relaxes. "He doesn't appear to have his axe with him tonight, anyway."

Dad and I walk halfway down the range to catch up with Old Tom, who is whistling in rhythm with the plunking of two shag bags onto range ball after range ball. The red shag bags are almost full. He continues whistling until we're within a few feet of him.

"Tom Morrison?" Dad asks.

"I am," the old man replies quietly. He plucks one final range ball and then stops in his tracks. "You must be Randy and Billy Black. I've been expecting you."

"It's a pleasure to meet you," Dad says. "I'm sorry to interrupt your work. May we have a few minutes of your time?"

"Of course," Old Tom replies, leaning comfortably on the shag bags.

He isn't scary at all. To my surprise, he seems quite pleasant.

"My son is in need of an experienced golf teacher, Mr. Morrison—"

"Please call me Tom," the old man says.

"Ah—yes, of course," Dad continues. "The problem is—Tom—his old man can't keep up with his progress. Ben Farr says you're the fellow who can—and we respect Ben's opinion."

The old man appears undaunted by what seems to me to be the greatest of compliments. "I am happy to spend time with any golfer who truly has an interest in learning—But I am no teacher."

Here we go again! How many days in a row will I be rejected? Gus was right! *He is just a range picker*! *What was I thinking coming out here*?

The old man's voice re-emerges, dissolving my destructive thoughts. "The game of golf is the great teacher, teaching us of ourselves and our world. Trained CPGA professionals are also superb teachers, dedicated to helping people learn and enjoy this wonderful game. My skill is simply in organizing one's approach to learning—and in pointing out the obvious, the basic. That is my specialty—*I am merely a guide.*"

The old man pauses and smiles. "Pursuits are simple. It is people who choose to be complicated. In the nineteenth century, Ralph Waldo Emerson wrote: 'To be simple is to be great.' As true today as always."

Old Tom's way is comforting, but indeed *unique*. Waldo who?

"I am happy to pay your fee to guide my son," Dad chips in.

The old man raises his hand. "There is no need. I am paid well," he says softly. "What you both must agree to is the following."

Dad and I stand silent in anticipation.

He continues. "Billy will be respectfully prompt for all meetings, without complaint. No excuses. Meeting times cannot be changed. No exceptions. Each meeting is planned purposefully. Meetings will be outside school hours. There will be no argument about activities chosen. Billy must have a pen and note pad with him at all times, as repetition and review will indeed be expected."

Tom pauses to ensure agreement to this point.

Our gestures of compliance are sufficient.

"Ben contacted me yesterday regarding your situation. I have taken the liberty to check the availability of all lesson locations. All have checked out well. Our meetings will be completed fully in two weeks. Are these parameters acceptable to you both?"

"Billy?" Dad asks.

"Sure," I say, startled by the apparent ease of progression.

"Then it's okay with me, Tom," Dad says. "You have a deal."

We each shake hands with Old Tom. His handshake means business.

Old Tom Morrison smiles at Dad and I as if we are one. "Know from the start that no pursuit exists to surpass the fabric of an unconditional loving relationship between parent and child. It is the essence of life. What is most precious is most simple. You will be far ahead to recognize this now." He stands comfortably. "Be back here on Wednesday at 5 pm, Billy. I will require just over two hours of your time. There is no need to bring golf clubs."

With a nod, the old man excuses us.

Dad and I thank him, then turn and walk away. The next stage of my golf career, however strange and secretive, is arranged.

As we walk outside of hearing distance from Old Tom, I bump Dad on the hip. "What did he mean by all of that 'essence of life' stuff?"

"I don't know, Billy," Dad says, "but he's right."

Chapter 3

The Big Picture

Wednesday evening finally arrives. I approach the driving range with a sense of nervous anticipation. I've been reeling uneasily these last few days, unsure of this old man's lesson plan. Or whether he would help me? Or hurt me? Or confuse me? I have zero idea if Gus knows I'm out here—with his range picker, nonetheless. And why no golf equipment? How can I learn about golf without golf equipment?

Our driving range is nestled to the right of the first fairway, separated by a few rows of poplar trees and high netting. The sound of a tee shot pinballing amongst the large trees and netting regularly signals the birth of another four-hour golf dilemma.

The range's anatomy is faintly rolling, starting level, then lowering before finishing on a bit of an up-slope. The delicate valley formed produces a brief blind spot. Otherwise, the range is quite functional. Flags of varying colours define standard golf-appropriate yardages. Netting encircles the range's sides and end. The South Saskatchewan River cliff provides the right border of the range.

The weather today has been symbolic of early spring in The Hat—cool, yet golf-able under clear blue skies, a standard-issue light jacket enough protection for most. An additional evening chill now pervades the air.

As I draw nearer to the unassuming, slightly leathery-faced old man, I decide he must surely be anticipating my arrival. For him, this is probably a rare opportunity to work with a player of my calibre. It'll be a notch on his belt, for sure. It's probably why he waived his fee.

Old Tom's look is not the look of your classic golf teacher. He stands about five-and-a-half feet tall, a half-foot shorter than me. His hair is light brown and thinning. An old, navy blue golf shirt and ragged jeans cover a thin, lean frame. The old man is busy emptying range balls into a large tub propped on the back of a golf cart. This is the person to whom I'm supposed to trust my golf game? Everything seems wrong.

He looks up. Without a break in the rhythm of his task or a change in facial expression, he greets me. "Good evening, Billy. What a beautiful day it has been."

Old Tom sets his shag bags down and approaches, seeking my right hand with his own. He places his left hand firmly on my right shoulder. His emerald green eyes affix mine. He shakes my right hand firmly. "I am impressed that you are prompt for our first meeting. You are mindful of my time—and your own. You will continue to earn my respect through more of the same mindfulness."

I smile half-heartedly. What's the big deal? What's with all the drama? This guy is a little *too* excited to see me. I've never had a response like this before *just* for being on time.

The old man saunters back to the cart to grab what appears to be a 7-iron. He re-approaches, squares his body to mine and once again fixes his stare deliberately. Old Tom Morrison presents his 7-iron gallantly in front of his chest, one hand supporting the shaft, the other carefully cradling the underside of the iron head, as if presenting a medal of valour. His stillness produces a dramatic silence—a silence that lasts a dozen seconds.

"This is a golf club, Billy," he finally proclaims and then pauses, allowing his conviction to take root. "Each golf club has a grip, a shaft and a head. Each head has a face. Tell me what part of the club this is."

The old man points to the shaft of the club and stares unflinching.

You've got to be kidding? Has this old crooner lost his mind? This *is* a big waste of time after all—just like Gus said! Doesn't he know who I am? I've won four junior club championships, three Southern Alberta Junior Championships, one Alberta Junior Championship and finished fourth at the Canadian Junior Championship—and he thinks I don't know what a shaft is?

The old man seems genuinely disappointed, yet speaks calmly. "You are not ready to be here if you do not know what part of the golf club this is."

"Of course I know what part it is," I blurt. "I just can't believe you're asking me."

"It is the shaft," shoots the old man. "No hints on the next one. What part is this?"

He points to the grip.

"The grip," I snipe back.

"And this?" the old man quips unwaveringly.

"The head."

"And this?"

"The face."

"What part of the face is this?"

"The toe," I spit.

"And this?"

"The heel."

"Very good. Let's move on."

The old man proceeds to review every golf club in the bag, providing in-depth details about lofts and lies, grips and grip sizes, shafts, shaft lengths, flexes and torques, kick points and shaft installation. He reviews swing weights, club weights and head designs. He briefly reviews the history and development of golf and golf equipment. With each second, the information becomes deeper and more fascinating. His knowledge of golf is impressive. He has my attention.

"*One* factor determines your future as a *participant* in this game, Billy. One factor alone. That is *character*. The game of golf tenders a dynamic mixture of both struggle and enjoyment to its participants—similar to life, really. Those unable to welcome the constant company of each will visit the game only briefly. Struggle is the supreme builder *and* tester of character—and golf holds dearly people of character."

"*Two* factors determine your ultimate position as a *player* in this game. Two alone. The first is *character* and the second is *skill*. Golf cannot be faked, Billy. In time, your strengths—and weaknesses—will be well exposed."

"You are far ahead to know right now that *skill* in golf is largely based on the execution of a few fundamental cornerstones. Master these fundamentals and maximize your skill level. It is that simple. You will receive what you give—you will reap what you sow. Work *hard*, but also work *smart*. Remember the acronym 'FSF,' Billy." Old Tom nods in the direction of my lap. "Please write it down."

I scramble to regain control of my pen and note pad. I had become so enamored by the old man's words that I had been neglecting my note taking. Two pages already lay full of frantic scribble. I flip to the next page and write 'FSF.'

"It is an acronym for 'Fundamentals Solid First.'" He pauses as I write. "Resist the learning of any further information of your subject until you are absolutely confident you have mastered its *Fundamentals Solid First*. Adhere to this acronym and progress most efficiently—in any pursuit." He smiles mischievously. " Notice that 'FSF' is also an acronym for 'Fun-

Struggle-Fun', the great recipe for skill and character development. Nothing meaningful is ever accomplished without challenge, Billy. Call on 'FSF' regularly for guidance."

I scribble.

Old Tom looks at the candy bar in my free hand. I hadn't eaten after school and was hungry, so I grabbed it and a soda in the clubhouse on my way out here.

Old Tom continues. "I find it helpful to pick a parallel subject—for simple comparison—as I guide a student through the idea of fundamental cornerstones. This way, you will easily grasp that pursuing golf is no different than pursuing any other activity. I pick a subject where I sense a student may lack knowledge."

He pauses and again glances in the direction of my *supper*.

"It appears that you may benefit from a parallel to the subject of health. Three hundred years ago, Dr. Thomas Fuller, the British scholar, preacher and physician said: 'Health is not valued 'til sickness comes.' If you intend to play this game at a high level, I can assure you that your health will play a great factor. It will be time well spent."

I feel like an idiot. I don't eat that many candy bars normally. I was just too busy to stop for a bite. I do drink a lot of sodas, though—which didn't seem to hurt pure-hitting Canadian pro Moe Norman any. Or did it? I've heard that the legendary eccentric used to drink a dozen or more sodas per day.

Old Tom continues. "Golf and health each have four cornerstones. I will parallel the two as we talk. Enjoyment will be yours when you grasp the true value of fundamentals and simplicity. Mastering cornerstones results in clarity and in ease of progression, both in the short- and long-term."

The old man's temperament never wanes from the start, despite my obvious rise in attentiveness. He seems like the real deal, like golf truly is a part of him. But there is more to this man—much more. I can feel it.

"You must learn to excel at the fundamental cornerstones of your chosen discipline and never waver. Never be distracted by short cuts, tips or fads in your pursuit. Be forewarned that to do so requires much discipline and focus. Short cuts will surround and tempt you always. When you truly believe that you understand and have mastered your fundamentals, set aside time for occasional review. Review more often when you struggle—and, rest assured, Billy, you will struggle. Problems will almost always relate to the execution of a basic fundamental or fundamentals, no matter what your skill level." He looks at my candy bar and soda again and smiles. "Your supper choice will cause your health to struggle."

I blush momentarily.

Old Tom continues. "The level of excellence that one achieves is dependent firstly on one's ability and willingness to gain knowledge and understanding of the cornerstones of one's pursuit. Yet knowledge and knowing are two very different terms. One cannot *know* until one can *do*. Knowledge is only the beginning."

"Excellence secondly depends on one's ability and willingness to apply this knowledge. Knowledge gained means little until properly applied. Application includes creating a clear vision of short- and long-term goals and on establishing strong work routines. Make the conscious choice to apply knowledge as habit. James Garfield, the twentieth president of the United States, once said: 'Ambition itself never gets anywhere until it forms a partnership with hard work.' Apply your knowledge properly, Billy. Form good habits. Be prepared."

"Lastly, excellence in any pursuit is dependent on one's knowledge gained from the experience of application and from review. The cycle repeats as knowledge from experience is gained. Never underestimate the power of reviewing even the most basic fundamental, even as additional knowledge is gained."

The old man pauses, accentuating the importance of these principles. "Remember these three factors and you will learn quickly. Please write them down."

I write as he recites:

1. Knowledge

2. Application

3. Review

"You will use your time efficiently by employing this simple formula in the pursuit of learning fundamentals. Seek knowledge from proper counsel in order to delineate central from peripheral, primary from secondary, major from minor. Never attempt to gain further education until you have truly mastered your fundamental cornerstones through this formula. Once you grasp *Fundamentals Solid First*, little else remains in comparison. Your time will be spent most efficiently."

I am mesmerized as the old man continues to speak with ease and sincerity about learning fundamentals. Have I ever really learned them in golf? I know I haven't. On this point, my golf education had been all over the map. A tip here, a tip there, anything I could get my hands on. I've always considered myself more of a *feel* player. Maybe that's just been an excuse to be lazy. I've always had a deep-down sense that something is missing in my approach to the game. Now I'm sure of it.

Strangely, I've also always considered myself a student of the game. Old Tom Morrison is making me see that I've been kidding myself. I'm a genius around my friends who know little or nothing about golf, but I can barely open my mouth around him, for fear of being discovered a fake. Ben said that Old Tom is someone special. I can see he's right. It's time for me to *really* learn this game.

Old Tom continues to speak in his rhythmic manner. "We are all human and most humans become cocky at the first sign of what they see as *success*. Cockiness stems from ego. Ego leads to laziness and impatience and to a misunderstanding of the pursuit—to a misunderstanding of life itself. Ego prevents one from mastering and often even acknowledging fundamentals. Forget ego, Billy. Ego isn't real but to the egotist. Aspire instead to be true to your deepest nature—be caring, honest, patient and respectful. You will find happiness and success everywhere everyday. You will experience the true grace that is life. You will progress most efficiently."

With that, the old man leans the golf club against the cart and grabs the shag bags. "See you back here on Friday at 5 pm."

Frozen in a daze, I want to ask a hundred questions. Who are you? Why do you pick range balls? Where did you get so much golf knowledge?

I can sense by the old man's actions that there will be no questions tonight. It has been quite a meeting—nothing like what I had expected.

Holy cow! What time is it? I've been so enthralled with Old Tom, I haven't noticed that the sun has almost gone down. I check my watch—7:25! Man, I feel like we've been here fifteen minutes!

"I didn't realize how late it is, Tom," I say. "I'll be late to pick Leah up if I don't—"

I look up.

Old Tom Morrison is fifty yards down the driving range fence line, picking range balls in the near darkness—whistling.

Chapter 4

The First Cornerstone

I arrive at the driving range Friday at 4:55 pm. Old Tom is already seated by the practice tee, his chair facing down the range. I approach him from behind. His golf club leans against the right arm of his chair. He appears to have some sort of exercise device on his left hand. He is squeezing and opening his hand against the resistance of the device. Open—close—open—close. Over and over again. I've never seen this before.

"What's that?" I snap, trying to startle the old guy.

Old Tom continues the exercise silently, then calmly speaks. "It's an important golf lesson. One you'll never forget." He turns to make eye contact with me. "It's the first cornerstone of golf, Billy—*the grip.*"

He wasn't shocked at all by my sneaky arrival. This old dude is centered! Old Tom has such a youthful fascination with everything. I keep forgetting he's probably three or four times my age.

"Looks like hand exercise to me," I quip skillfully.

"Hand muscle balance and hand strength play a great role in the proper golf grip— and in golf longevity," Old Tom replies, as he switches the device from his left hand to his right. "When your hand muscles are strong, your grip pressure can be light—a great advantage for most all shots. In deep rough, strong hand muscles can be called upon to square the clubface and penetrate, despite the grab of the grass. When hand muscles become imbalanced from repetitive gripping, injuries to the hand, wrist and elbow are common. These are the most common injuries in the sport. Keep your hand muscles strong, balanced and elongated, Billy."

"I use a racquet ball," I say in defense. "I only grip the ball. I don't open my hand. Is that wrong?"

"You're not doing an exercise poorly, you're doing a poor exercise." Old Tom looks at me kindly. "You have taken on poor counsel. You have gained poor knowledge."

"I guess I just did the same exercise I saw everyone else doing."

"Too bad," he says, without emotion. "Good thing golf pioneers like Vardon, Zaharias, Horton Smith, Jones, Rawls, Hogan, Player, Nicklaus and Woods did not think your way. It was Einstein who wrote: 'Few are those who see with there own eyes and feel with their own hearts.' Do you *only* want to be like everyone else, Billy?"

I shake my head. Sounds like my Dad talking.

"How many muscles are in the hand, Billy?" Tom asks poignantly.

"I have no idea," I say, bewildered by the depth of his question.

"Eighteen," Tom replies. He stares at his own moving hand, leaving time for me to process his answer. "How many of those eighteen muscles do you think close the hand?"

I shrug.

"Nine," he says serenely.

Tom holds his hand clenched on the device for effect. Then, he powerfully stretches his hand wide open, challenging the device's elastic finger bands, and holds. "How many muscles do you think open the hand?" he demands.

Tom's hand strength is impressive in both directions and his point is clear.

I smile. "The other nine, I bet."

The old man nods. "The best approach is always the simplest. To find the simplest approach, gain knowledge from proper counsel. The same exercise principles exhibited by this simple hand exercise device apply equally to the rest of the body, minding the body's performance demands for strength *and* balance *and* circulation. Proper exercise compliments every facet of your game—and your life. Think for yourself, Billy. Consider the contribution of all muscles that act on each body area. Prepare your body properly for performance." Tom's smile reflects the effortlessness of his words. "Gain knowledge of cornerstones from proper counsel, apply your knowledge as habit and review regularly."

"Like your 'This is a Golf Club' bit on Wednesday?" I quip.

Tom slips the device off of his hand. "This one is for you. It is a *Handmaster*. Strengthen all of your hand muscles in balance to achieve maximum grip strength. You were headed for hand muscle weakness and imbalance. I wish every golfer had one of these."

I smirk, realizing *school is in*—we're well into today's lesson. Tom gets his messages across with such ease.

"What you must accept now, Billy, as if it were law, is that your success in golf is directly dependent upon how well you understand and apply the proper grip. It is your only physical connection to the golf club. When the grip is mastered, it squares the clubface consistently and transfers power from the body to the clubhead. You may be tempted to give up on your pursuit of the proper grip when results are not immediate. Grip changes may be awkward. Stick with them. Perseverance here will separate you from others." Tom grabs the iron that's leaning against his chair. "Remember the three P's of the proper grip. Please write them down."

I grab my pen and pad and write as he speaks.

1.   Power

2.   Position

3.   Pressure

"*Power* is the first *P* and is gained through proper exercise. We have already talked about power. Check the last two *P's* every time you grip the golf club."

Tom stands and grasps the club in his left hand.

"*Position* is the second *P*. Remember that every player is physically unique, Billy. All have different heights, postures, strengths, flexibilities, arm lengths, hand sizes, finger lengths and finger thicknesses—even different goals. Work with your CPGA professional to find the grip position that is best for you."

Tom pauses for me to gesture that I am following.

I am.

"Always remember that the body performs best as it approaches *neutrality* in any given function. Find the proper individual grip position by finding the position where the hands lie most neutrally on the grip handle. As the hands accelerate during the golf swing, they seek this same neutral position. Observe this next exercise and be well on your way to understanding grip position."

Tom sets up in a posture as if to hit a golf shot, except his hands are apart. His weight is slightly more on his right side and his hands hang limply. His posture is athletic. He is holding the iron loosely in his left hand.

Suddenly Tom begins to pass the handle gingerly between both hands, while the club head remains stationary on the ground. He maintains his posture throughout the exercise and comments: "When one assumes a proper golf posture and allows the arms to hang freely, the hands naturally assume their most neutral and unabated position. Pass the grip handle back and forth to get a conscious snapshot of the position that the handle desires to lie in each hand."

Tom pauses momentarily as each hand receives the club.

"First, let's examine the handle position in the left hand," he says. "Most will find that the club handle lies naturally in the middle of the index and middle fingers and then more toward the base of the pinky finger. But remember Billy, all golfers are unique." He then lifts the club off the ground, gripping only with his pinky, ring and middle fingers. "Discover the natural role of the left hand's heel pad by supporting the club in the three *grip fingers* of the left hand—the pinky, ring and middle. The heel pad naturally provides the roof of the stable left hand grip, the fingers the floor."

Tom sets the club back onto the ground, passes the club handle lightly between each hand a few more times and stops as it arrives in his left hand. As advertised, the grip lies slightly diagonally in his fingers.

I smile.

"Apply light grip pressure with the left pinky, ring and middle fingers."

"Light grip pressure?" I ask.

"Let's cover this right now," Tom returns confidently. "It is the third P of grip—*Pressure.*"

Tom shuffles to square his body to mine.

"Give the clubhead a tug when it comes to you, Billy," he says.

Tom again holds the club in his pinky, ring and middle fingers. His thumb and index finger are off the handle, forming a charade handgun. He slowly lifts the iron by hinging his left wrist, until I can see the upside-down "7" on its sole. Tom nods, so I give the clubhead tug. It's in there fairly snugly, yet his wrist wiggles.

He comments: "Notice that when you pull on the club, my body does not move. This is the proper grip pressure—light. If I were to have gripped the club too firmly, my wrist and elbow joints would have stiffened. Your small tug would have pulled my body forward, off-balance."

I feverishly scratch notes, yet I still don't quite grasp his point.

"Interesting test, Tom," I say, "but how does this relate to golf? My grip pressure is surely firmer than yours. So, why light pressure—in golf swing terms?"

"Four important reasons, Billy."

I am ready with pen and pad.

"*Reason number one.* Small muscle groups are less likely to repeat a given action than large muscle groups. When a golf shot is dependent on the action of large leg, core, torso and back muscles, the chance of repeating the action is high. When a golf shot depends on the action of smaller hand and wrist muscles, the chance of repetition is much lower."

"Think of how a choir sounds, Billy. A choir of thirty singers has a more consistent sound than a duet. The duet sounds very different if one singer is even slightly off-key. Not so if one singer is slightly off-key in a thirty-member choir. The largeness of the group dampens the overall effect of the action of each individual."

"The same is true with muscles. Larger muscles contain many muscle fibres, like the members of the large choir. The overall affect of the large number of muscle cells dampens the affect of each individual muscle cell. Small muscles produce less consistent actions because fewer individual muscle cells contribute. The golf swing is performed using large leg, core, torso and back muscles, with very little dependence on the conscious actions of smaller hand and wrist muscles. Grip pressure must be light."

"*Reason number two*. Tightness in the smaller forearm and hand muscles interrupts the transfer of centrifugal force from the body to the golf club. When your hands are firm, you lose power."

"The martial arts illustrate this point best. Students are taught that a relaxed muscular state allows optimal transfer of force, from opponent to student in defense, and from student to opponent in attack. Contracted muscles react inefficiently in transferring force. In golf, relaxed hand muscles mean power, accuracy and consistency."

"*Reason number three*. Tightness in smaller forearm and hand muscles ruins balance. When you pulled slightly on my club to test my grip pressure, what happened to my body?

"Nothing," I say.

"Exactly. Yet, had my grip pressure been excessive, your gentle tug would have pulled my body forward, off-balance."

Tom raises his iron once again and gestures for me to repeat the test. I tug. His grip pressure is suddenly very firm, causing my tug to pull his body forward.

"Correct?" His eyebrows rise.

"Correct," I reiterate with a chuckle.

"This same small tug occurs on the body as the mass of the club head accelerates during the golf swing. Tight hand muscles pull the player off-balance in the same way."

I nod and smile again, enjoying Tom's examples.

"*Reason number four*. Tightness in smaller forearm and hand muscles can ruin pace and timing. We will talk more about this later. For now, understand that the body must lead the arms and hands slightly during the swing. The hands play a reactive role. Grip the club tightly and invite a tendency for the hands to act early and quickly, sacrificing power, accuracy and consistency. It is the main reason golfers hit poor shots on first tees. Fear of failure and embarrassment increases anxiety and, in turn, grip pressure, leading to poor pace and timing—and poor shots."

"You've spent some time thinking about grip pressure, eh Tom?" I offer sarcastically.

"Grip pressure is part of a cornerstone, Billy. Strive to understand it well," Tom returns sternly. "Now, let's move on."

Old Tom still holds his seven-iron in the three fingers of his left hand. His thumb and index finger remain outstretched. He gestures towards the two with a tilt of his forehead. "These two fingers are the *glue fingers* of the left hand. They are used to connect the left hand to the right. Interlock or overlap the pinky finger—the *glue finger* of the right hand—between or behind your left index and middle fingers. Either an overlapping or interlocking approach to the union of the hands is fine, a simple matter of comfort. Have a CPGA professional check your position and explain your options."

"When the left hand wraps onto the handle, the left thumb lies to the right of the handle's centerline, the index finger to the left. The 'V' formed by the two points at or just to the right of the player's chin—never right of the shoulder. They are connectors only, supplying zero in grip pressure."

I don't feel like I quite understand Tom's *neutral* bit yet. My grip probably needs work and I want to gain proper knowledge. I'm eager to clear this point up.

"The 'V' made by my left thumb and index finger points more toward my right shoulder, Tom" I say, "or maybe even more right. I see my hands aren't neutral, but I still don't see the problem."

"One's grip is never a problem until the club accelerates during the swing motion," Tom answers at once. "As the club-head accelerates, its mass increases substantially, in turn increasing the hands' quest for neutrality. When hand position at setup and impact differ, inconsistent squaring of the clubface results. Position the hands initially as they will desire to be during acceleration. Very simple."

I am following well so far, as I've studied grip to some extent already. Still, I am eager to have a CPGA professional, like Ben Farr, double-check my left hand position.

"Bring the right hand around and onto the handle." Tom says. "The space between the thumb pad and the heel pad of the right hand fits like a puzzle piece onto the left thumb. This is very important. Be sure to sense this sensation. The hands are gluing together, now able to act together, as one."

Tom sets his golf club down for a moment. He touches the tips of his right thumb and pinky finger together and points at the cleavage that has formed at the base of each.

"This space here," he says. "Make sure the left thumb glues in here in a snug fashion."

Tom wrinkles his brow until I nod.

"The middle and ring finger are the *grip fingers* of the right hand. They supply light grip pressure."

Another brow wrinkle by Tom. I nod, acknowledging the third P—*Pressure*—once again.

"The right index finger and thumb lay gently on each side of the handle centerline—the thumb to the left, the index finger to the right. As with the left hand, they contribute nearly zero in grip pressure. They form a 'V' that agrees in direction with the 'V' formed previously by the left hand. They are the *garden fingers*—along for beauty mostly, but are quite indicative of how well the rest of the grip is cared for." Tom looks up. "The two hands are now prepared to work as one."

"That's a pretty long speech about grip, Tom," I joke. "You better come up for air."

His expression remains unchanged despite my obvious comedic prowess.

"Once knowledge is gained, conscious repetition is your next step."

"Conscious repetition?" I echo.

"Apply your knowledge consciously before each shot until the proper grip becomes an unconscious habit. Away from the course, train by holding a club in the three *grip fingers* of the left hand and then alternately in the two *grip fingers* of the right hand."

Sounds tiring.

"How long does it take to become an unconscious habit?" I ask.

"Who is to say?" Tom says casually. "You must be caring and respectful in your pursuit—there is no timetable. You must be honest—consciously repeating your proper grip each shot. You must be patient—your body will accept the habit on its own schedule."

"Are you saying that I should check my grip even during practice?"

"Every shot," Tom returns. "Don't fret, Billy. You will find *excelling* to be enjoyable. It is the reward of honest work, caring, respect and patience. When your proper grip becomes unconscious habit, review it regularly, three or four times per year—review more when you struggle."

"Wow," I sigh. "That sounds *tough*."

"It is much less tough—and much more satisfying—to learn cornerstones properly the first time," he smiles. "Accrue knowledge. That is your first step. Understand *why* your hands are where they are. Understand grip pressure. Next, apply your knowledge. That is your second step. When the application of cornerstone knowledge becomes habit, review regularly. Review is the third step of learning. Apply this three-step strategy to learn all cornerstones—you will excel."

"Gain knowledge, apply and review. Got it!" I say excitedly.

Tom looks away in thought. "Meet me in the golf course parking lot tomorrow at 4 pm sharp. I will require two hours of your time. You should leave now, Billy. You have homework."

"I do?" I ask, somewhat confused.

Tom glances at the hand exercise device.

"I'll get started tonight."

Chapter 5

Redcliff

I check my watch—it's 3:45 pm on Saturday. I sense a unique excitement about spending more time with Tom and don't want to be late. He's always complimentary about punctuality. I don't want to let him down.

I played this morning for the first time this year. Our spring has been cool thus far. Today is the first day of play on the regular *permanent* greens. The greens get covered for protection each winter. Temporary *winter* greens are created in their place in the fairway.

The permanent greens usually open April 1st, a week or two after the final snow thaw. Unfortunately, the course is in extremely poor shape this year, a result of untimely spring weather. An early thaw followed by a late freeze has caused rampant *winterkill* of the grass roots in low-lying areas. Our grounds superintendent, Andy Cameron, will whip them into shape in no time, I'm sure. He'll soon have some warmer weather to work with. The Hat is considered to be *the desert of Alberta* and is usually the first city to get onto permanent greens.

Today I was also able to sneak in forty minutes of putting drills after my round. Short game is the strong suit in my game. I feel like I have as much touch around the greens as anyone, a factor that has helped lower my scores more than anything else.

I wonder if Tom, or eventually maybe Ben, will try to change my approach to my short game. It will be an interesting summer, indeed. I'm glad Dad talked me into spending time with Tom.

I hustle back to the club storage to pack my putter and practice balls into my golf bag. Then I saunter over to the parking lot. Tom is already waiting, seated peacefully in his truck, a dark blue Ford Ranger. His left arm rests chicken-winged on the base of the open driver's side window.

Tom looks up at me and then peeks at his watch. "Hop in. I must run and get some groceries. My wife, Thelma, is making a Greek salad. We can talk as we go."

I crawl in on the passenger side and pull the door shut. Groceries? Oh well, maybe some driving time with Tom will be good anyway. Maybe I can ask some of the endless questions I have. How does he know so much about golf? What type of player was he? What level did he play up to? Why doesn't he have a teaching business? Did he teach the same stuff to Ben? When is he going to look at my swing? Why does he pick range balls?

Tom pulls out of the parking lot and heads up the drive. "In the next few weeks we are going to break the golf swing down into four fundamental cornerstones," he says. "Grip was the first. We have three left to study. Master them all and your game will be strong for life."

That sounds good to me.

"Now what of health, Billy? As promised, it is our parallel subject." Tom is silent as he negotiates the course's winding exit road. He reaches the main street and speaks enthusiastically. "Is health any different to learn than golf? Is any subject any different to learn? Accrue knowledge of fundamentals, apply your knowledge and review regularly. Move on only when fundamentals are mastered. Can health, like golf, truly be broken down into simple cornerstone principles? Or is health too complex? Can each person take control of his or her own health by mastering cornerstones?" Tom peeks at me whimsically and smiles. "You will find true health to be very simple."

I can see I am really going to pay for having that candy bar and soda during our meeting on Wednesday. What a waste of an evening. I'm here to learn about golf, not health.

"Your body requires four necessities to survive, Billy," Tom says. "These are the health cornerstones. Four only—just as in golf. The health of your body mirrors the degree to which each is supplied daily. Go ahead. Try to name something your body must have in order to survive."

I gaze into space.

Tom smiles and hints further. "Something that, if it were unavailable to you, would cause your body to die."

It's fresh on my mind and provides an opportunity for confession. "Well, before our first lesson, I felt like I was going to starve to death, so I bought a candy bar and a soda. My body needs food to survive. Food must be one."

"Bingo, Billy! You have figured out the first cornerstone of health—*food*. A most important subject at this time of your life."

"You know, Tom, I really don't eat that many candy bars—"

"Food is as central to your health as your grip is to your golf swing," Tom says, without acknowledging my sniveling. "'Let thy food be thy medicine and thy medicine be thy food.' Hippocrates wrote that in the fifth century before the birth of Christ. It is a very famous saying. Please write it down."

I pull my pen and pad from my knapsack and begin writing. "Got it," I say.

"Let thy grip be thy connection and thy connection be thy grip," Tom continues. "I said that just now. It is not a famous saying at all. Write it down anyway, for comparison."

I chuckle to myself nasally. Tom's sense of humor is healthy, but subtle.

"They are direct parallels," Tom continues. "Neither is less important to its topic than the other. Both are rock solid cornerstones. You can have a poor grip and still play golf. You can have a poor diet and still live. Yet, you cannot play *well*, nor live *well*. You most certainly cannot play to your maximum potential, nor live to your maximum potential. Most will never experience maximum potential of either in their lives. That is fine, if by free choice—free choice to be mediocre."

"Free choice—to be mediocre?" I question.

"Golfers may be unaware of the import role that their grip plays in the success of their golf game. Similarly, people may be unaware of the import role food plays in their health. This changes once one is made aware of the value of a cornerstone by proper counsel. Ignorance is no longer an excuse for poor choices. Instead, one is now able to choose freely their future. People may choose to excel, to be mediocre or to be lacking. Results are never haphazard."

I notice that we have driven past many grocery stores and are now nearing the edge of town. "Where do you grocery shop, Tom—Calgary?" I ask. More comedic prowess.

"We are on our way to visit my good friend, Jerry Colter. He owns the best greenhouse in Redcliff."

Redcliff is the small sister city to the west of The Hat.

"Did you know that Redcliff boasts to be the 'Greenhouse Capital of Western Canada'?"

I didn't.

"When one receives proper counsel in the cornerstones of their pursuit, they are immediately empowered to choose their future." Tom turns toward me in challenge. "You have been made aware of the importance of grip. What you do with this knowledge is your choice."

"I choose to excel," I say, confident in my ability to do so.

"Walk talks louder than talk talks, Billy," Tom says pleasantly. "Let your actions alone speak. You will save much time and energy."

Tom signals for a left turn off of the short stretch of TransCanada Highway between Medicine Hat and Redcliff.

"You will be empowered once again today," he says.

We soon arrive at a huge greenhouse and are greeted by a tall, Scandinavian-looking man with curly blond hair.

"Welcome, Tommy. Come on in." The man seems genuinely pleased to see us. "Our selection is excellent today. Thelma is making her Greek salad?"

"She is," Tom says, smiling. He fans his arm toward me. "I have brought a visitor today. Billy Black is curious to discover how candy bars are grown."

The two men laugh heartily at my expense. I turned beet red.

"Maybe you can show me some other options," I croak sheepishly.

"It's a pleasure to meet you, Billy." The man extends his large hand. "I'm Jerry."

"Nice to meet you, Jerry," I mumble.

Jerry's handshake nearly crumbles my hand.

Once inside, I notice a sudden sense of life and freshness. I've never been inside a greenhouse before. Jerry leads us up and down long aisles, pointing out various vegetables. It's fascinating. He offers us sample after sample of different types of cucumbers, tomatoes, peppers and lettuce, all surprisingly delicious.

I'm impressed by Jerry Colter's endless energy—it reminds me of Tom's. I notice that the skin on his arms and face is smooth and healthy and his frame is lean and muscular, though he must be in his late fifties or early sixties.

Jerry bites into a yellow pepper and turns to me. "My body knows by nature exactly what to do with this pepper, Billy. It wastes very little energy digesting it and receives immense nutritional value from it. The same is true for everything you have sampled today. Your candy bar, however, is a much different story."

I slouch in embarrassment.

"You're not alone, Billy. I don't see many kids your age in here—it's a damn shame, too! Not many of our *leaders* today encourage kids to discover the value of proper nutrition. Advertising dollars aren't spent with the intention of making fresh fruit, vegetables and herbs appear very cool. Kids naturally choose processed junk food and soda over real food— just as their *heroes* have asked them to. Maybe you will be more responsible with your endorsements if you are a famous golfer someday. Maybe you will have a positive influence on kids— and many others."

It's nice of Jerry to acknowledge my golf potential, but the mini-adulation session doesn't last long.

Jerry continues. "When the sugar from your candy bar enters your blood stream, a very dangerous series of events begins. The body initially is amazingly adaptable, no matter what it is fed. Early organic changes to the body are silent, yet symptoms *will* appear eventually—if food choices are not changed. Symptoms are the body's friendly warning flag, occurring when the body can no longer adapt to its owner's poor choices. Our health care system rewards people for acting on quieting these helpful symptoms, rather than addressing the true reason for their cries. And Canada's system is supposed to be one of the world's best!"

Jerry and Tom roll their eyes in unison.

Jerry finishes his yellow pepper and continues. "Sickness has progressed well along its path by the time symptoms make their appearance. Symptomatic people have been sick for years in most cases. They are already well behind the 'health eight-ball', so to speak. Many ultimately *discover* symptoms of illness and disease and then chase them around like cat and mouse the rest of their lives—usually with drugs and surgery. Drugs and surgery—that's not health care—that's *disease care*—an expensive and backwards approach to health. No health care system can be efficient or fiscally responsible based on treating symptoms."

Jerry steel blue eyes swiftly focus on me alone. "When the refined sugar from that candy bar is absorbed into your bloodstream, many dangerous processes are set into motion. One of the first is your pancreas flooding the bloodstream with insulin. A high level of insulin in the blood is terrible for the body yet is a necessary reaction, an attempt to control the suddenly high blood sugar levels—something your body monitors very closely. A high level of insulin promotes the production of fat and cholesterol in the body. Say *hello* to a life with a higher risk of heart attack, stroke, diabetes, cancer and many more *fun* challenges. A high level of insulin also decreases the release of growth hormone and the absorption of Vitamin C by the white blood cells, which depress your immune system. These are just a few examples of the chaos sugar causes in your body."

He stops for a moment. "Do you feel like a candy bar now, Billy?"

"Not really," I say. I mean it, too. I'm full from testing the vegetables!

Jerry checks his watch and continues. "Candy bars are an excellent snack choice if you desire high levels of cholesterol and fat in your body and if you enjoy being sick. Maybe your girlfriend prefers you chubby, I don't know. Or maybe your future family doesn't want to know you for very long. Or maybe you aren't *that* serious about golf after all. Is that why you choose sugar for your snacks?"

Jerry stares at me curiously.

"I just didn't realize it was that bad for me. I was in a rush, I—"

"Sugar consumption," Jerry cuts in, ending my excuses, "is commonly associated with diseases like diabetes, cancer, heart disease, stroke, arteriosclerosis, hyperglycemia, hypoglycemia, mental illness, dental deterioration, hyperactivity and even the common cold. I could go on and on if I had more time. Refined sugar is toxic to your body. Read about it, Billy. Go on the internet. It's easy to find information nowadays. The connection of refined sugar to health problems is not a secret anymore. Read books like Sugar Blues and Sugar Busters. Either way, stay away from refined sugar and simple carbohydrates."

Before this, I had no idea how bad that candy bar was for me. Jerry's explanation is something I needed to hear, I guess. Better for my golf? Better for Leah? Better for my future family? Wow. But no more candy bars? What kind of a life is that? Maybe a healthier, longer and more successful one.

"Strive to regularly consume a variety of fresh fruits, vegetables and herbs, preferably in their most natural state. Eat several smaller meals daily rather than fewer large ones. Your body is efficient at breaking down and using small, regular, fresh meals without producing large insulin spikes. Think in terms of *nibbling* five or six times per day, rather than *gorging* two or three times. Take the time to chew your food, Billy. You will enjoy and appreciate its taste and texture and assist digestion. Strive to feel *light and fulfilled* rather than *stuffed.* Learn about proteins, fats, carbohydrates, vitamins, minerals, trace minerals, essential fatty acids, fibre, enzymes, antioxidants and pH. You'll find diet to be a most rewarding and interesting study. Consult a naturopath, dietician, nutritionist or other health care practitioner, to determine what foods and eating habits are best for your specific body—that of an up and coming hotshot golfer!" Jerry winks at me. "Don't waste your talent on sugar and refined foods, kid."

I nod respectfully, acknowledging Jerry's heartfelt advice.

"You're on your own now, fellas. Make yourself at home. I have an order to prepare for a local market. Good luck, Billy."

"Thanks for showing me how candy bars are grown, Jerry," I wave cheekily.

Jerry nods and smiles, then fades into the far corner of his greenhouse.

*

Tom continues to pick out various vegetables as we walk. With each selection, he names the item, comments on its nutrient content and health benefits, and places it in his basket. "As in golf, most people skim past health cornerstones, looking elsewhere for easy tidbits—short cuts, potions and quick fixes. Their answers have almost always been plainly in front of them all along." His expression changes subtly to invite challenge. "Once one learns the cornerstones, *health* is merely *choice*."

"It was by choice I choose that candy bar the other day," I say. "I guess you're saying I shouldn't eat candy bars anymore."

"I am saying you should be aware of your choices, Billy. You will make many important decisions everyday in your life. Gain knowledge, act and review. The sum of your choices is who you are. Today you have received counsel on diet from an expert—you have learned of the ills of refined food and sugar. The choice of your action is your own, based now on properly accrued knowledge. I have no control on your decisions."

Tom grabs a few cucumbers and throws them into his basket. "Most choose the easy way rather than the healthy way, even when they know which is best. They find comfort in old familiar habits and instant gratification or they may have a deep-seated need to fit in with a majority. These folks will never truly excel in their pursuits. They fear change and resist growth. Mediocrity and frustration are the sum of one's choices, as are success and happiness. Be aware of the central importance of choice. Think for yourself, Billy. Act for

Redcliff 45

yourself. Change, in life, is a given. 'Am I changing for the better?' is the question?"

Tom loads half a dozen red peppers into a plastic bag. He directs the open bag toward me. "The choice of your actions—and your path—is always your own."

I reach in, fish out a small pepper and nibble as we continue to walk.

Chapter 6

Cruisin'

When Tom dropped me off after our greenhouse tour Saturday, he asked me to meet him in the club parking lot today, Monday, at 5 pm. He says we'll go on another trip, a very short one this time. It will take about an hour. What trip could take an hour? I look for Tom's truck. Nothing. It's about a minute before our meeting time.

I snuck in an hour on the range and a half hour in the practice bunker between school and now. I even checked my grip and began to work on some changes. Tom is right. The changes do feel awkward. I rushed from the practice area to get here. I do respect Tom's time—and my own.

He and his truck are still nowhere to be seen. This is unlike him. Where can he be? What could make him late? Is he okay? I continue to roam the lot.

At five o'clock on the nose, a high-pitched beep disturbs my search. What the heck is that? I survey the parking lot and see nothing. Then another beep, this time louder, closer. I ramble in the direction of the somewhat annoying sound. Nothing. The next beep, however, tells me I am very close.

Finally, camouflaged between two mini-vans at the far end of the parking lot, there is Tom—and he isn't in his truck. To my astonishment, he is seated on the driver's side of a shiny blue *motorcycle* complete with *sidecar*. He shoots out one last shrill beep blast, for effect. I stand there staring dumbfoundedly.

"There you are, Billy. I've been waiting." A proud smirk beams from beneath a bulky black motorcycle helmet. He's clearly proud of his coup.

"Yeah? And I've been looking!" I snigger, entertained by the sight of Tom and his rig. "What could this possibly be?"

"An important golf lesson," he says, as calm as ever. "One you'll never forget. Check out the plates." Tom extends his neck briefly, gesturing to the rear of the vehicle.

I circle back and study the plate: "ALNMNT".

"Alignment." I announce, in partial victory.

"The second cornerstone of golf, Billy—a*lignment*. Often overlooked, often misunderstood, but a very simple concept." He points inside the sidecar. "There's your helmet. Hop in. Let's go for a ride."

"Why not?" I chuckle.

The vehicle lets out a loud roar as Tom fires it up. Carefully, he backs us out from between the vans—the motorcycle sidecar is parked tightly. He turns the lead tire to exit, gives it throttle and raises his legs onto the footholds. We're on our way.

I've never even seen a real sidecar before, let alone driven in one. It is a unique experience! Tom drives without speaking for a few minutes, allowing me to enjoy the sensation of the fresh open air.

He soon begins speaking in a tone loud enough to overcome the noise of the vehicle. "There are two alignment lines in golf, Billy. One is the *TARGET* line. The other is the *POWER* line. The TARGET line extends from the ball to the target. The clubface is aligned down the TARGET line. The feet, hips and shoulders of the golfer are aligned down the POWER line. The POWER line is parallel to and left of the TARGET line. Each line is equally important in the golf swing." He hesitates momentarily. "Quite similar to the alignment of this motorcycle and sidecar, really."

"Golf swing alignment and a motorcycle sidecar— similar?" I return. This is news to me, but not to Tom. He makes his case immediately.

"In a sidecar, the passenger—*you*—represents the *golf ball*. The motorcycle driver—*me*—represents the *golfer*. You are aimed down the TARGET line. You are indirectly going for the ride. I am aimed down the POWER line. I am directly supplying the power and direction necessary for your travel." He becomes silent momentarily as he changes lanes in the now busy downtown rush hour traffic. "What would happen to you if I were to forget that I had a sidecar attached to the motorcycle? What would happen if I began to drive with only one alignment line, like a regular motorcycle?"

I study our surroundings and process his question. "In this traffic, I would probably be crushed into that truck in the lane to our right," I say, noticing the hungry tires of a wine-coloured Ford F350 a few feet to my right. "Wherever you are directed, I'm always that much more to the right. No need to show me this one for real, Tom. I think I get it."

"Good observation, Billy," Tom smiles. "I would have gladly stuffed you under that truck if it meant teaching you this most valuable cornerstone."

We both chuckle.

"Most golfers are not clear about this cornerstone. Most see one alignment line—the TARGET line," Tom said. "They unknowingly align their body to the TARGET line thus aiming the clubface well to the right."

"Just like the side-car passenger—*me*—being shoved to my right, into that truck," I observe.

"Correct, Billy."

I think about the principle for a minute, but it doesn't add up. "How come I don't see everyone's golf balls on the right side of the golf course then, Tom? Wouldn't that make sense if what you say is true?" I'm onto something.

"Good observation, Billy. You are beginning to think for yourself. You will continue to grow by doing more of the same."

Tom slows and turns into a small parking lot. He then circles the vehicle back in the direction of the golf course—a move possibly signaling *mission accomplished.* That, or we're just running out of time. The traffic is much lighter as we drive away from the busy downtown area.

Tom continues. "Most golfers *do* suffer this alignment problem and instinctively make adjustments to keep the ball on line. Otherwise, most golf balls *would* end up to the right of the targets, as you have suggested. Listen closely, Billy—this next point is very important." The rhythm of Tom's speech slows markedly. "The *symptom* of this alignment problem is that the ball ends up to the right of the target. What is the *cause* of the symptom?"

That's easy. "Poor alignment," I say.

"Excellent," Tom says. "And what solution corrects the symptom?"

"Correcting the alignment."

"Based on what?"

"Based on the knowledge of proper alignment lines— target line and power line," I respond, wondering what his point is.

"Good," he chirps, becoming even more intense. "What if I told you that most people do not correct their alignment in this case? What if I told you that most people instinctively turn, or *close*, their clubface—making the clubface also point to the target?" He relaxes his expression and continues. "The symptom of the ball going to the right is mostly gone—Poof! No more problem. Do you think this is a good solution?"

I don't know what answer he's looking for, but it doesn't matter. I think for myself now. "I don't think it's a good solution at all," I say confidently. "They still haven't addressed the original alignment problem."

"But now their ball doesn't end up to the right of the target, which makes them feel good," Tom argues. "They have corrected the problem."

"Yeah, but now their clubface is always going to be closed," I say in defense. "They'll hit the ball too low. That's no good! It's a cover-up for the original alignment problem, not a correction. And it starts another problem—low ball flight!"

"Excellent, Billy!" Tom nods happily. "You have just explained perfectly the concept of the OCF—the *Original Causative Factor.*"

I scramble for my notebook. Tom waits.

"To address the OCF requires that one determines and attends to the absolute root cause of any symptom, as opposed to addressing the symptom itself. When we address only the symptom, we usually introduce *new* problems, called *side effects.*"

"That's a mouthful, Tom," I laugh in mid-scribble.

"It is a most valuable concept in golf and in health and in life. Make sure you understand its meaning. ***The OCF can almost always be traced back to the poor understanding or execution of one or more fundamental cornerstones—in any pursuit.***"

Tom orchestrates a well-planned silence before guiding my thoughts further. "Did you notice a health cornerstone as we drove in the downtown traffic? Much was presented to you in this brief period."

"No—I didn't," I said hesitantly. "Unless the cornerstone was 'avoid crashing into big trucks.'" Classic line.

Tom is not amused by yet another example of my snappy humour. "Wrong, Billy. What did you find different about being in the sidecar at the golf course compared to downtown?"

I refocus, immersing myself in thought. What was different? "The drive was refreshing near the golf course, but really uncomfortable downtown," I conclude. "I've never noticed how bad the fumes are during rush hour traffic. It was difficult to breathe."

"Another excellent observation, Billy!" Tom's face lights up, "based on an important health cornerstone. If your body doesn't have it at all, you will die. What is it?"

"Air!" I say triumphantly. "The body needs air to breathe or it will die".

"You are very right, Billy," Tom says from underneath his shiny sphere. "Health cornerstone number two—*oxygen*. The body needs a constant supply. All cells need oxygen to survive and to perform their functions. Like food, the degree to which you avail yourself a fresh supply of oxygen is mirrored in your health expression. Golf course air is better for your body than downtown traffic air. Air pollution, like smoking, leads directly to ill health. In the short-term, it reduces the oxygen available to the lungs and therefore to the cells of the body, limiting the cells' ability to function. In the long term, it reduces the lungs' ability to even attract and absorb oxygen. Despite the many warnings, 25 per cent of our population still smokes. Seek clean air and learn to breathe properly, Billy."

Tom pauses to adjust his helmet strap.

"Strive to take advantage of full cycles of inspiration and expiration," he continues. "The German fitness legend, Joseph Pilates, wrote: 'The first lesson is that of correct breathing.' If *he* felt this strongly about proper breathing, who are *we* to argue? Most of our population breathes inefficiently, though many books are available on the subject. Dennis Lewis, Donna Farhi and Robert Fried are excellent authors, if you are curious."

It's difficult to take notes in the sidecar, but I do. I *am* curious!

Tom drives in silence allowing another important health cornerstone to sink into my brain. Minutes later, the lesson continues.

"What else can be done to improve the body's supply of oxygen?"

"Avoid taking golf lessons with you, Tom," I quip. "I could barely breathe downtown." Still more comedy from the kid!

"What else?" Tom returns promptly.

What else helps me use oxygen? "Exercise?"

"Bingo." Tom smiles. "Regular exercise improves all facets of your health—and your life—directly improving how your body makes use of oxygen, leading to efficient blood flow. It is blood that transports oxygen, as well as nutrients, throughout the body, cleansing and invigorating all of its cells. The body adapts to the environment into which it is placed. Make sure your environment is regularly active. Participate in swimming, biking, walking, hiking, roller-blading, aerobics or another such activity. Your body will transport oxygen—and other nutrients—most efficiently."

"I feel like I'm in Biology class, Tom." I complain.

"Your body is a constant biology class," Tom retorts joyfully. "You might as well understand its basic principles. Golf is the best reason I know to learn about the body. Most golfers spend all of their time and money on the *minor equipment*—the clubs. Yet a much greater cost is paid for not keeping up with the *major equipment*—the body. Strive to truly know your equipment, Billy."

Tom pauses to make the right turn that leads into the golf course.

"An understanding of proper breathing principles and oxygen metabolism is vital during a pressure-packed golf tournament. *Breathing*, *relaxation* and *performance* differ mostly in spelling. Otherwise, they are terrifically close relatives. Unmonitored breathing often becomes shallow in times of challenge and struggle, compromising performance and health. Learn to breathe properly now to ensure the utmost chance for success—and ease—in the future. Acquire every edge possible."

"You better get me out of this sidecar then," I say eagerly. "I can't read about proper breathing in here—and I certainly can't get any exercise."

Tom makes the looping turn that leads to the straightaway to our clubhouse. As we drive, the adjacent eighteenth hole catches my eye as never before—the early evening shadows hit the fairway and green beautifully. I am especially conscious of the fresh golf course air. What a magnificent place—and a magnificent sport.

"Now, a pop quiz, Billy."

Tom yanks me back to reality.

Two men lean on their minivans on either side of Tom's parking spot.

"You can see that I do not have much room to park this vehicle. Tell me about my alignment lines. How many do I have and what are they?"

I shuffle upright in my sidecar seat and focus acutely on the parking spot.

"You have—two alignment lines. One is the TARGET line, which I am on. The other is the POWER line, which you are on. The POWER line is parallel to and left of the TARGET line. Be equally aware of each when parking a motorcycle and its sidecar *and* when setting up for all golf shots."

"Well done, Billy," Tom smirks his approval.

He parks perfectly in the small space available and turns off the vehicle.

"Meet me here in the parking lot at 3:45 pm on Wednesday. The meeting will take three hours and will be well worth every second."

"I'll be here," I say as I jump out of the sidecar and slip off the helmet.

Spending time with Tom has been exhilarating. I feel like I am truly getting a grasp of the significance of cornerstones.

Without a word, the two men retreat into their minivans and drive away.

Chapter 7

Exempt

I arrive home after my alignment lesson and am greeted by a look of curiosity on Mom's face. She says nothing, but her expression begs my questions.

"What?" I say.

She holds her grin. "Nothing, Billy. Is there a law against a mother smiling at her son?"

I don't buy it, nor does Mom want me to. Her mysterious smirk remains.

"Did—someone call for me?" I ask.

"Two people," she squeaks, like air escaping from a tire stem.

"Should I guess or are you getting ready to tell me?" I chuckle.

"Leah called," Mom says.

"Great—and who else?"

"Ben Farr wants you to call him," she smiles. "He said it's important, Billy."

"Ben Farr phoned for me?" I ask excitedly. "What did he say?"

"He just said it was important and that he wanted you to call him back."

Mom passes me the note with his phone number.

I stand frozen in thought. What could he want? Is he going to teach me? Is it about Tom and I? Or just about Tom? Maybe he wants to play golf with me? The weather is getting better—wouldn't that be an experience!

"Well, Billy," Mom derails my runaway train of thought. "What are you waiting for? Call him already—and don't forget to phone Leah."

I force my mind onto the act of dialing Ben's number. My heart pounds like a punk rock drum beat. Imagine, *me* returning *his* call. What am I going to say?

"Hello?" A female voice answers.

I hesitate.

"—Is—Ben there—please?" My voice is nervous and crackly.

"One moment please."

I start to sweat. I can barely breathe. What's wrong with me? Wait a minute. I'm the best junior player Medicine Hat has ever seen. Why would I be nervous talking to Ben Farr? So what if I'm phoning my boyhood idol. Who cares? He's just another person. No big deal.

"Hello," comes Ben's voice calmly.

My breathing is a step out of rhythm.

"Oh—ah—Hi—ah—Ben," I stutter, as my heart races. "It's Billy—Billy Black—calling—my Mom said that you were—trying to get—that you had called."

There it is, my first ever phone sentence to Ben Farr. Sure, not my best stuff—I admit—but it came off all right!

"Yes, Billy." His voice is slow, soothing and rhythmic. "Thank you for returning my call."

"No problem—Ben." I attempt to be casual. "What—ah— can I—do for you?"

We're just two buddies having a buddy-to-buddy conversation. No big deal. I'm euphoric inside!

"I don't know if you are aware of it, Billy, but I am on the city's tournament committee. I represent the Connaught Golf Club. Pat Janzen from your club and Larry Lanz from the Redcliff club are the others on the committee."

I am suddenly frozen, speechless and lost.

Ben continues. "I spoke with Tom Morrison yesterday. He has been impressed with your attentiveness and enthusiasm."

"He has?" I say by reflex. "You'd sure never know it."

"That's Tom's way, Billy," Ben replies. "He doesn't have peaks and valleys in his life. His way has no opposite. He speaks of simple truths, having no need to over-glorify nor hold hatred. He is objective and simple and lives in peaceful bliss. His way is very healthy."

I nod uncomfortably in silence. *That's* a bit for me to process.

"He will have a very positive effect on your life," Ben adds.

"He already has, I think," I say excitedly. "Did he have a positive affect on yours?"

"The biggest," Ben offers immediately.

An awkward silence.

"Billy, the reason I phoned is that Tom and I feel it would be beneficial for you to get your feet wet with some stronger competition. The Victoria Day Golf Tournament is held at the end of May each year. I spoke to the committee about getting you an exemption into the this year's tournament."

"An exemption?" I echo.

"Yes. It's a men's tournament, ordinarily limited to players eighteen years of age and older. The committee agrees that it would be a positive situation, both for the tournament and for yourself, if we exempt you from this requirement."

"Wow—that's pretty cool—" I stammer, unsure exactly what all of this means—or how I should reply.

"You must first respect the importance of the tournament, Billy. You may know that Victoria Day is a very special day for Canadians. It is a national holiday. The Victoria Day holiday falls on the first Monday before May 25th each year, originally in celebration of Queen Victoria's birthday, May 24th, 1819. Because of the warm spring in Medicine Hat, the Victoria Day Golf Tournament has become a cherished and sought-after title for some of the best golfers in and around Alberta."

"I never knew what Victoria Day was, Ben," I say meekly, "but I've dreamt about playing in it for years now. I've even pictured myself winning it."

Ben replies rhythmically, unaffected by my brash statement. "First you must speak to your mother and father. It would be a new level of competition and a new challenge for you. Your parents must have a say."

"No problem, Ben. I'll talk to them tonight," I say, now giggly with excitement.

"Drop by my pro-shop tomorrow night at 7:30 if you decide to enter. We can fill out the forms together. I have agreed to sign for you personally."

Ben's tone remains unchanged throughout the phone call. Mine bounces around like a jumping bean.

"Thanks, Ben," I say. "I'll probably see you tomorrow night."

"See you tomorrow night, Billy," Ben says. "Bye for now."

"Good bye, Ben."

Our first conversation is over. It went pretty well, too. Very well. And Ben Farr thinks I'm ready to play with the men. Why did he say: "See you tomorrow night?" Was he giving me his opinion of what I should do?

Many times I've been on the practice green at the golf course pretending to have a ten-foot putt to win the Victoria Day Tournament. Sometimes I make it, sometimes I don't. When I make it, there is no better feeling. What if I win it for real this year? I've always known I had to be eighteen to get in, so I've never taken it too seriously. All that has changed now. Dad wants me to take action and I want to play. I'm dizzy with anticipation.

Mom, Dad and Danny have already eaten supper. Mom had put together a plate of leftovers for me earlier, as she often does. I retrieve it from the fridge, throw it into the microwave and hurry into the living room. Mom and Dad are watching TV. Danny is already out for the evening.

"Mom—Dad—can I talk to you?"

"About Ben?" Mom asks.

"Yeah, kind of," I answer, still stirring.

"Bring your dinner into the living room, Billy," Dad says. "I'll set up a TV tray for you."

I hustle back to the kitchen, grab my meal and rejoin Mom and Dad in the living room. The TV is now off. I explain everything Ben said.

Dad is first to react. "What do *you* think, son?" he says.

"I want to do it, Dad. I want to see where I stack up against these guys."

"It'll be a whole new level of competition for you, Billy." His tone is balanced between concern and celebration. "I'm behind you if that's what you want."

One down, one to go!

"Mom?"

"As long as you have fun, dear," Mom smiles lovingly, "I'm with you, too."

"I will, Mom," I say excitedly, my mind racing through the possibilities. "I promise."

"Now phone Leah back," Mom says.

*

I show up the following night at the Connaught pro-shop around 7:20. The shop is empty, as the afternoon had been cold and wet. Very few people would have played today. Before long, Ben walks in from outside. "Just finishing up, Billy," he says. "Would you like some green tea? It's cool tonight."

"Sure," I say. "I've never had green tea before."

"It's very healthy," he replies. "Tom got me on to it years ago."

Ben signals for me to follow as he locks the pro-shop doors. He then leads me into a small office and plugs in a kettle.

"I've noticed Tom's a pretty healthy guy," I comment nervously, digging for a vein of information.

"He sure is," Ben smiles. "Do you know how old he is?"

"No."

"Guess."

I think for a moment.

"Sixty?"

"He'll be seventy-five next month," Ben says.

"Holy cow. I never would have guessed."

"And he never would have told you," Ben replies with a smile. "I found out from a mutual friend in Texas a few winters back."

Ben flips through a stack of papers before pulling out two. I assume they are my entry forms for the Victoria Day Golf Tournament. He hands me one of the papers and a pen.

"Fill this out, Billy."

It's a basic entry form. How does he know I'm going in? He didn't ask for my final decision. Ben is like Tom. He doesn't wastes words or time. He's efficient with every action.

I begin to fill out the basic form—name, address, phone number and the likes.

"Do you spend your winters down south?" I ask.

"Yes, a few months every winter," he responds, matter-of-factly.

"Playing?"

"Yes—some. I also spend a lot of time with my wife and my kids and a lot of time reading and teaching." Ben spoons what looks like pine needles into a teapot.

"Do you miss playing regularly?" I dig further. "Is it hard to be in the pro-shop instead of playing tournaments?"

"I have many enjoyments in life, Billy," Ben says kindly. "Professional golf used to consume my life for all the wrong reasons. It is now one of many pleasures for me. I don't miss the way I used to live, no."

"Wasn't it exciting?" I press on.

"If I were more healthy, it probably would have been the most exciting experience I could imagine. I learned from Tom that my mind—my ego—wouldn't allow me to enjoy it in a necessary way. I focused mostly on what I didn't possess, rather than on the miraculous blessings I did. I tried to make the game my own, unknowingly putting myself ahead of it—an illusion that can never survive. The game is what it is, a great teacher and a great friend to everyone. It is honest and bigger than any one player. It will certainly outlive all of its students. Nobody can claim golf as his or her own. My old way of thinking ended the only way it could have—in frustration, confusion and disappointment."

"What happened?"

"Tom happened," Ben says, unplugging the steaming kettle. "What I considered success on tour didn't happen soon enough or correctly enough for me. I quit playing and took a job here at Connaught under Don Gray."

Ben pours hot water into the teapot and replaces the lid.

"Green tea has many positive health benefits, Billy. It reduces the risk of cancer, heart disease and chronic illness. It also reduces blood sugar, blood cholesterol and inflammation and slows aging, among many other benefits. You may take a can home with you if you wish."

He hands me a sealed green can with Chinese printing on it.

"Thanks," I return.

"On tour, we used to say that becoming a CPGA club professional stood for *Can't Play Golf Anymore*. I took this ridiculous notion to heart for a long time. I was miserable. I drank a lot and nearly lost Sarah and the kids many times. Tom was the only person who could see what was going on. Goodness knows I couldn't. He saw I was in need of simple, basic direction. Tom saved my life by guiding me towards simplicity."

Ben pours green tea into two cups and hands me one.

"He taught me about fear, the illusion of ego and the danger of claiming the game as my own. He led me to understand my own grace, a realization that has since given me a deep sense of peace and happiness. I am finally healthy after ten years of booze—and even drugs, Billy. He easily got through many layers to my core. I never truly understood the value of basic cornerstones, though they were right in front of me all along in this wonderful game. I was too busy watching how good golf looked on me. My mind kept me from seeing more in the game—and in life. I started putting gratifying short cuts before fundamentals. It nearly killed my golf game, my health and my relationships."

"Tom taught you golf cornerstones like he's teaching me?" I ask.

"Yes, he did," Ben says.

"Did he pick another subject as well?"

"Yes, he did."

"Did he use *health* with you, too?"

"No, Billy," Ben says. "My parallel was *relationships—* caring, honesty, patience and respect—the four cornerstones of all relationships, whether with yourself or another. Tom showed me how peace and happiness are available to all of us right now by committing to these four simple principles. He picks a parallel where he sees a student is especially weak. You think you're learning about golf, but you're learning the parallel as much, if not more. In truth, the parallel is usually much more important—and contributes to better golf anyway." Ben chuckles. "Most folks won't listen when they're preached to about a weakness. I know I wouldn't have. Most people are controlled by their mind, their ego. He told me he would show me the joy inside the game of golf, which got my attention. Instead, he showed me the joy in life, which spills into everything."

"You were a tour player, Ben," I say gratuitously. "Did he actually help you with your golf game?"

"He's got golf in his bones, Billy, in his fingernails, in his breath. I've never had it to that depth, though I'm close now. He loves golf because he sees it as a true teacher of life. I was never truly able to relate golf to life until I met Tom. I was only capable of relating it to *me*. The same things that kept me from being free and happy on the golf course kept me from being free and happy in my life. I'm happy about life now, appreciative and content—and probably a better player now than when I was on tour. Rather than feeling ashamed about not *making it* as a player, I'm honoured and excited to observe and live by the passion, teachings and fundamental applications of this great game—and I enjoy passing them on to others." Ben smiles almost shamefully. "I used to feel like a fake. I wouldn't even teach my own family and friends because of boredom. Now I do eagerly. Now I understand the importance of sharing my passion. I'd say he helped me with my golf game, wouldn't you?"

I nod, moved by how much respect Ben has for Tom—and for golf.

During our conversation, I had completed the first form. I slide it over to Ben. He switches it with the other form.

"This form you and I fill out together, Billy. It acknowledges that you have agreed to act respectfully during the golf tournament—no swearing or temper tantrums or the likes. Our committee is using you as a test case for allowing future young players into the tournament. Use this opportunity wisely. It will affect many, not the least of which is *you*—as do all actions. Read it and sign it, if you are agreeable."

I read the form and sign it, agreeing that it is appropriate. Ben takes the form, signs it and staples the papers together. He folds the papers neatly and tucks them into an envelope that has already been addressed and stamped.

"You are with a very special man right now, Billy. Strive to learn. And remember, everyone struggles. True learning is a process. Be honest and consistent with your effort, and remain patient. I know how much effect Tom can have on a person's life perspective. Remember, I took the course."

We finish our tea. Ben takes the cups and sets them aside.

"Ben, why doesn't Tom charge me for his time?" I ask. "He looks as if he could use the money."

"Tom has plenty of money *and* income," Ben says casually. "He charges others enough to overlook the fees from some of his younger or misguided projects. And rest assured, the folks he works with regularly can afford him."

"Does he teach professional golfers?"

"Tom calls it *guiding*."

"Which players does he guide?" I meddle.

"That's not important," Ben smirks. "Any more questions, detective?"

I hesitate, but have to ask. "Why does Tom pick range balls?"

Ben chuckles. "You'll have to ask *him* that one. He may even answer you."

Ben's tone clearly says I should ask no more questions about Tom.

"Thanks for this, Ben—getting me into the tournament, I mean," I say.

"Thank me by setting a good example," Ben returns with a smile.

Fair enough, Ben Farr. I'll do just that.

Chapter 8

Great Seats

I walk to meet Tom in the golf course parking lot at 3:45 pm on Wednesday, as instructed. He's lounged back in the seat of his pickup, putting the final touches on a helpless apple. He chews steadily and rhythmically, then pauses and looks up as I approach. Both windows are open.

Tom swallows, peeks at his watch and smiles. "Hop in. Let's get going. The first show starts soon. No need to worry, Billy. I already have the tickets. They are as far from the stage as possible—the best seats in the house for what we need to see."

"See what, Tom?" I ask.

"An important golf lesson, Billy. One you'll never forget."

I can't help but chuckle to myself, like a toddler readying on Christmas morning.

Tom drives down the hill that supports the golf course, leaving the Crescent Heights area of The Hat. He takes the Maple Avenue Bridge across the South Saskatchewan River— the river that splits the city into north and south. After the bridge, he takes the first left, heading towards "The Arena", our town's main entertainment facility.

The Arena is the home of our local WHL junior hockey team, The Medicine Hat Tigers. They're what the Packers are to

Green Bay, what the Cubs are to Chicago. If you live in Medicine Hat, you love The Tigers and you root for them—as if by contract. The parking lot is packed. Families are haphazardly making their way towards The Arena's entrance.

"The Tigers are playing an afternoon hockey game?" I ask.

"Some *tigers* are," Tom smiles. "The circus is in town. It's the best opportunity for you to learn about the third cornerstone of golf—*balance*. But we're not here to see the tigers. It's the tightrope walker that will teach you so much if—"

"If I think for myself!" I shoot out smartly.

Tom is unaffected by my genius. "Never sacrifice balance for anything in any part of your game, whether it be in putting, chipping, pitching, bunker shots, trouble shots, half shots, three quarter shots or full swings. All must be performed in balance, in control. Golfers would save a lot of frustration by learning the role of their legs, butt, spinal curves, chin and shoulders in achieving balanced shot making—they could all use a trip to the circus."

With that, he parks the truck. We hop out in unison and begin our walk to the building. Tom moves quickly with little effort. When we reach the entrance, he points out a large mural of a hockey player painted on the wall.

"There is much to learn about balance by observing high-level hockey players as they skate. Lessons are everywhere, Billy—you are learning to see them. Teachers are everywhere—when we look."

He's right. I'm beginning to notice skills in other sports and activities. I look forward to discovering more parallels with this new way of thinking.

We enter The Arena and begin looking for our seats. We start near the floor, yet move away as we search. Where are we going, I think to myself? Tom finally settles into a seat that is as far away from the floor as possible.

"Ah, here we are, Billy," he says.

"Nice seats, Tom," I blurt sarcastically.

"Their great seats, Billy," he returns. "We were lucky they were still available. They are the best seats in the house to see how a well-trained athlete deals with the challenge of extremes of balance."

"A tightrope walker—a well-trained athlete?" I return dryly.

"Definitely. And more like a golfer than most any other athlete—mentally, physically and conceptually—when it comes to balance. The two are nearly identical, only one is clearly more difficult." Tom motions toward the darkened tight rope. "Errors are easier to make on that rope and much more penal. If golf demanded balance like tightrope walking, golfers would improve quickly. You will observe today how the body's wisdom reacts to true extremes of balance."

I laugh to myself—Tom's continual respect for other activities is refreshing.

"I'll be right back, Billy," he says. "Save my seat."

No one is within five rows of us.

I smirk and nod.

A crowd of mostly children and parents continues to fill the vacant seats near the building's floor. A saturating smell of popcorn compliments the enthusiastic Arena atmosphere.

My thoughts wander back to when I first met Tom and how he conveyed to Dad and I that no matter what he plans I will not argue. This must have been what he was referring to. A week ago, I certainly wouldn't have felt comfortable going out in public with some old range picker—I would have felt ridiculous. My thinking has expanded tons since then. I'm not only comfortable now, I'm eager to hang out with Tom—even at a kids' circus!

Tom arrives back carrying two bottles of water and two sodas. What is this all about? What's he up to this time? The scene is humorous, as the old guy is clearly preparing to guide.

"Two cornerstones for the price of one today?" I quip wisely.

No reaction.

"The third cornerstone of health, Billy," he replies. "*Water.*"

"What about the two sodas?" I ask.

"Choices."

Tom hands me one of each of the drinks and keeps one of each for himself.

"We have some time before the circus begins," he says, settling in. "Why not make use of it?"

My mouth salivates for the soda.

"If you have not yet heard, Billy, your body is made mostly of water—approximately seventy percent, give or take a bit. It is a fairly well known fact." He pauses. "The brain is made of a higher percentage."

Mr. Tracken's biology class sure is coming in handy these days.

"I think I've heard that before," I say.

"Some experts feel strongly that water is a common life denominator, linking generations, even civilizations, even universes. Many essential lessons can be learned through the study of its form and function. Unfortunately, our modern desire for instant wealth and gratification has led to an erosion of our world's water supply. A day will arrive when, as a planet, we will be forced to review our ways."

Tom is freaking me out a bit. What does he mean by "erosion of our water supply?" I suddenly feel thirstier than ever before.

"Nutritional experts counsel us to drink a minimum of eight glasses of clean water daily. A more specific formula offered by Paul Chek of the C.H.E.K Institute in Vista, California, advises us to drink one ounce of water daily for every two pounds of our body weight." He turns to me. "How much do you weigh, Billy?"

"About one fifty," I reply.

"Then strive to drink seventy-five ounces of water daily— nine or ten eight-ounce glasses—to be maximally healthy." Tom performs one of his calculated pauses. "How much water *do* you drink per day, Billy?"

"I'm not gonna get to have this soda, am I?" I ask.

"The choice will be yours, Billy," he says. "First, you must gain knowledge of your choices. How many glasses of water do you drink per day?"

I settle back in my seat. "I guess I drink about 4 or 5 glasses a day, a little more when I play golf." Not too bad, I think.

"If the body does not get a proper supply of water, a state of dehydration exists," Tom warns. "The structure and function of every cell in your body is completely dependent on water, Billy. Water is the body's common solvent, 'the soup of life', as Japanese water researcher, Dr. Masaru Emoto, puts it. Every action requires and takes place in water. Water is responsible for both the separation and transportation of substances within the body and for the elimination of toxins out of the body. All cells and tissues, including those in the stomach, brain, lungs, heart, intestines, skin and muscles work most efficiently when properly hydrated. If all body functions are affected by improper hydration, it stands to reason that *lack of water* is a component in most every disease process."

Whoa, disease? When did we start talking about disease? This is just water, right? Just thirst? You can't say disease and thirst in the same breath. I can accept what Tom says about water and performance, but I don't have any disease—even if I do drink a lot of soda.

"C'mon, Tom. I don't feel like I have any disease," I say defensively. "You're being a little dramatic about water, aren't you?"

"Tell me how you know for sure, Billy," Tom challenges.

"Know what for sure?" I return.

"That you are free of disease."

"Well, wouldn't I feel sick?" I argue—I'm getting a little more freaked out.

"Recall Jerry Colter's counsel, Billy. An visible disease state takes time to build. Diseases develop silently, at a cellular level, well before the body begins to signal for help through symptoms. Do not fall into this common trap. Cancer is still cancer before pain and weight loss is evident. Tumors do not start the size of a golf ball. Arteries are well plaqued before shortness of breath and the pain of a heart attack beckon. How you feel has little to do with whether or not a disease state is ultimately present. Do not make the mistake of gauging your health by gauging your symptoms."

"Is that why people get check-ups?" I ask.

"Yes," Tom says. "It is also why daily health cornerstones must be understood and acted on. Daily health choices determine one's health. The American author Henry David Thoreau wrote: 'Every man is the builder of the temple called his body'. Poor daily health choices may be causing sickness even though one is completely unaware of such. Daily health choices add up, whether proper or poor." Tom breaks for a sip of water. "How do most build their temple, Billy? They begin healthy habits upon *feeling sick* and discontinue them upon *feeling better*, a very dangerous health strategy."

"What about how you're born, Tom—your genes?" I ask. "That's the biggest health factor of all, isn't it? What can you do if you're born with something?"

"A good question, Billy, and certainly a valid point," Tom nods pleasantly.

I can tell he's happy that I've engaged myself in this subject.

"I am speaking specifically of health *choices*, Billy. Genetic make up is a given, a health starting point, per se. Indeed, our own start is out of our control." Tom pauses to prepare his point. "Be aware that after birth, health cornerstone laws become universal. Apply them well and health potential rises. Apply them poorly and health potential suffers. Be sure to accept that health cornerstones affect the health of all individuals, independent of state—whether healthy or sick, old or young, short or tall, male or female, black or white, thin or heavy. No one is penalized or exempted."

"Just like golf cornerstones apply to all golfers?" I ask, in review.

"The same, Billy. Individual variance may exist in the degree to which each cornerstone can be applied," Tom says, speaking with care. "A child confined to a wheel chair may not be able to exercise the same as you or I, yet his or her daily oxygen supply is still reflected directly in his or her health expression. A golfer with rheumatoid arthritis may not be able to grip the golf club in a classic way, yet his or her grip is still a key determinant of performance. The best available choice or course of action must be pursued by each individual, based on proper counsel."

I nod keenly in understanding.

Tom sets his soda under his seat, grabs his water bottle and twists open the cap. He raises the bottle to me in "cheers", takes a gracious swig and replaces the lid. "A proper supply of water is necessary for every living cell, tissue, organ and system in every living organism. Very few health situations require moderation of water consumption—kidney disease can be one. Most people are aware enough to hydrate for performance. Society as a whole would do well to discover that proper water intake more importantly maximizes health and prevents disease."

I am suddenly craving water. "Maybe they don't know about health cornerstones like we do," I say heroically, setting my soda on the floor. I follow Tom's lead by twirling the cap off of my water bottle and taking a swig. The water tastes more refreshing than ever before. I can somehow sense now how much I require it.

"Continue to seek counsel from the experts, Billy—naturopaths, dieticians, nutritionists, physicians and other health care professionals. Read books, an excellent source for information on all cornerstones. Start with Batmanghelij and Emoto, two most interesting water authors. Each will open your mind to the immense value of water. Once educated, make daily choices based on proper knowledge. You may empower yourself to replace poor health choices with hearty ones." Tom pauses mysteriously. "You have just gained crucial counsel for performance in golf, as well, Billy. Acquire every edge—think for yourself."

Tom settles into his chair. His posture is upright without being stiff. Like clockwork, as if Tom is controlling the show, the lights dim and a ringleader magically appears in the beam of a spotlight. Children's excited cheers dominate the crowd noise. The circus is about to begin.

*

It's been at least five years since I've been to the circus. My body feels vibrant as I drink water and enjoy the skilled performers—trapeze artists, lion tamers, clowns, acrobats, and even trained elephants. I consciously sense myself becoming an independent thinker and eagerly anticipate the learning of the third golf cornerstone. I feel excited, sensing how this time spent with Tom will strengthen my golf game and my golf career. So much is out there for me to accomplish. My mind wanders dreamily through the many possibilities. Sure I have lots to learn, but I feel like I'm taking the right steps. The old man beside me is widening my horizons. Most certainly, he is changing my life.

My thinking is interrupted as the tightrope walker is finally introduced. The spotlight speeds upward to the platform at the end of the tightrope. Tom nudges my knee and casts his chin upward to where a man stands in a spotlight holding a pole horizontally across his chest. Not surprisingly, our seats afford us an excellent view. We're as close to eye level as possible, perfect for observing the tightrope walker. He'll start from our right and move across to our left. At the center of the rope, he'll be directly across from us. Great seats!

The ringleader recites relevant statistics, including rope thickness and its height off the ground, further dramatizing the tiny margin for what could be large error. The Arena crowd falls silent.

Tom leans toward me and speaks in a whisper. "When learning any principle, search for the most extreme example that exists. Look no matter what or where the example is. You will gain a deep understanding of the principle without being distracted emotionally by the familiarity of the rest of the event. This is *balance*, the third cornerstone of golf."

A drum roll sounds. The tightrope walker prepares to begin his trek.

Tom leans over again and whispers. "Observe his legs, butt, lower back, shoulders and chin. Look deeply, Billy and this time observe with your *full being*, not just with your eyes. Sense what the tightrope walker senses. Feel what he feels. Putting yourself in other's shoes is a good practice in life, as well. You will learn much, not the least of which is patience and respect."

Tom's brow rises seeking my nod of comprehension, which I give.

"No matter which direction he moves or what trick he does, there exists only one centre of gravity to which he reacts. One true centre at all times, just like in golf. In a few minutes, tell me what you have observed."

I stare at the man on the rope, preparing to observe with my *full being,* as Tom suggests. I am suddenly feeling an immense nervous respect for this performer—legs, butt, low back, shoulders and chin.

The crowd applauds courteously as he easily makes his first pass across the length of the rope. Next, he crosses the rope backwards. This time, he moves much more slowly, allowing an excellent opportunity for observation. I am completely involved in each movement, a fascinating experience. A few times, he appears to lose his balance. Each time, I feel as if *I too* have lost *my* balance. Each time, the crowd lets out a collective sigh. A sense of relief floods The Arena audience as he crosses successfully.

The tightrope walker continues performing various tricks, including juggling and balancing on a chair. He is impressive and my first experience at *full being* observation is incredible. All too soon, the ringleader's voice cuts in, resulting in appreciative applause—and the beginning of the next act. In smooth progression, trained dogs begin circling below, attracting the spot light.

"Tell me what you saw, Billy," Tom demands loudly over the applause for the dogs. He is as excited as I have seen him yet—and I'm ready. I feel I *saw* a great deal.

"The first thing I sensed was the controlled pace and rhythm with which he moved. The only time his actions were quick was when he was off-balance. I noticed that his knees were always slightly bent, except on the leg he moved forward or backward in taking a step. Similarly, his lower back always appeared to have a very slight forward arch, even when he stepped. It was as if these angles absorbed his weight. His butt seemed to stick out and his shoulders were always level when he was in balance. When he was off-balance, the level of his shoulders shifted a lot."

I look over at Tom and pause to gauge his response. He is smiling and nodding, apparently impressed, but clearly asking for more.

"Oh yeah," I snap, recalling Tom's instructions to watch his chin, in particular. "His chin position stayed consistent, even when he seemed to lose balance. His chin remained relatively level, like what Mom bugs me to do at the dinner table."

"Your mother is a good judge of balance, Billy," Tom comments without emotion. "You are a sloucher."

I'm a little taken aback by Tom's abrupt and uncomplimentary statement. "I guess I slouch a bit—sometimes," I confess, "but I *am* pretty tall."

"You will never see a tightrope walker slouch. Heed your mother's advice, starting immediately."

Tom's posture is a constant reminder of his words. I shuffle to adjust mine. "Are we talking about tightrope walking now, or golf?" I ask.

"When it comes to posture, we are talking about everything, including health." Tom swigs from of his water and smiles. "When you train your posture at the dinner table or at your computer or in the classroom, you also train your posture for golf."

"Yeah, I guess." I mumble. I've never thought of it that way. "I find it tiring to sit up at the table, though. It's just easier to slouch. It's more comfortable."

"What is comfortable is not always what is best, whether in posture or in golf or in life." Tom says patiently. "Seek out what is right. Repetition will make it comfortable."

"Why does my dinner table posture affect my golf posture?" I ask.

"Muscles, Billy," Tom replies rhythmically. "When you sit properly, you are using, and therefore strengthening, postural muscles in your back, torso and neck. Just as in the proper grip, the stronger and more balanced your muscles are, the easier it becomes to achieve effortless results. Strong postural muscles allow effortless balance. Strong postural habits create strong postural muscles."

"So Mom's kind of my golf teacher too, eh?" I surmise.

"Your mother understands the principle of balance, something you must also understand." There is no joking in Tom's tone. "Seek counsel from chiropractors, physiotherapists, osteopaths, exercise therapists, fitness instructors and massage therapists. They are the specialists in spinal and postural balance. Learn about the balance-conscious exercise approaches of Pilates and yoga. Read books. Surf the internet. Learn proper posture—whether in sitting, standing, sleeping, lifting, playing music, running, skating, walking a tightrope or golfing. You name it. It is all the same—and all very simple. It is all *balance*."

I smile as Tom once again relates a golf principle to something other than golf. For some reason, this makes it easier for me to grasp and accept.

"To fully understand *body balance*, as in *grip*, one must understand what is *neutral*," Tom continues. "Follow me."

Without shifting, Tom levitates from his sitting position and glides up the remaining few stairs to the upper walkway. I struggle awkwardly to a standing position and follow.

During a Medicine Hat Tiger's hockey game, the upper walkway is reserved for "standing room only" hockey fans. During a circus, it's barren. A single light bulb auspiciously lights our section of the otherwise darkened walkway.

Tom startles me, having already situated his body perfectly square to mine, correctly anticipating the coordinates of my arrival. Immediately, he continues his guide.

"When we view the human frame from the front, *neutral* is quite straight forward. The shoulders are level, the pelvis is level and the spine and head are vertically straight up and down. In golf, our right shoulder tilts slightly low at address, permitting the right hand to be lower on the grip and allowing more weight to be on the body's right side—as is desired in the set up."

Tom turns his whole body around sideways such that his shoulders are now perpendicular to mine. He now faces the vacated tightrope.

"Confusion occurs when we view the human frame from the side," he says. "When the *neutral* human frame is viewed from the side—whether standing or sitting—the ear is vertically above the shoulder joint, hip joint and ankle joint, yet the *neutral* spine itself is not straight up and down."

I scribble notes and then realize that something doesn't add up. "How can the spine not be straight up and down, if the ear, shoulder, hip and ankle all line up?"

"A common question, Billy, and a good observation." Tom remains in his trademark neutral position. "Most all of the many bones of the spine are separated by flexible disks, akin to small flexible hockey pucks. These disks are designed to allow movement *and* efficient weight bearing. To accommodate biomechanically, the spine innately forms three distinct arches—a forward arch throughout the neck, a backward arch in the midback and a forward arch again throughout the low back. This fabulous shock-absorbing design protects any individual disk from being overburdened by the brunt of the body weight."

Tom purposefully slouches for illustration. "Poor posture voids this wondrous design, causing certain disks to be isolated, over-burdened and eventually damaged. Disks in the mid-neck and lower back are most at risk when spinal arches are not supported by their owner."

Tom is quiet in thought for a moment. "Arches are used in architecture in a similar way, Billy—aiding in balance, stability and weight distribution. Have you noticed that arches define some the world's most famous golf course bridges?

"I guess they do," I say, in reflection.

"Have you also noticed that arches are often used to support buildings?"

"Yeah, maybe I have—" I begin.

"The same is true of the spine," Tom says. From his neutral stance, he crosses his arms, bends at the knees and tilts his torso forward slightly from the hip joints. With minimal effort, he rotates his spine back, making a full golf backswing. He holds the position easily. "Understand and respect this wonderful three-arch design, Billy. Support it at all times. It is the centre from which all proper golf motions do or do not occur. It is the key to maximum position, balance and trunk rotation." Tom pauses. "Your slouching now clearly becomes a handicap."

"I'll take it more seriously, Tom—I promise," I announce.

He relaxes from his backswing position and smiles kindly. "Master the subject of balance, Billy—your spine *and* your golf game can last a lifetime."

"Like the tight rope walker!" I conclude.

Tom smiles proudly. "Your observations of the tight rope walker have been your best so far. You are learning pure observation. You noticed pace, rhythm, knee-flex, subtle low back hollow, stable butt position and consistent chin and shoulder level. All are great contributors to balance in the golf swing."

Tom pauses momentarily, allowing me to bask in my success, then speaks almost apologetically. "There are two observations I will add. It is quite unreasonable to expect you to have noticed these in the tightrope walker, as they are very subtle—two more reasons why our seats availed us the best view in the house. The same principles apply quite dramatically to balance in golf."

I stare at Tom, eagerly awaiting more information.

"A subtle angle is formed by the tightrope walker's legs and torso when viewed from the side. It is commonly referred to in golf as the *spine angle*. No variation occurs in this angle when a tightrope walker is in balance." Tom's tone becomes lower and more intense. "The spinal angle is an important tip-off to the balance of a golfer. It should remain the same throughout the golf swing. If you can observe this subtlety in a tightrope walker, you can easily observe it in any golfer."

Tom takes a sip of water.

"The last observation of the tightrope walker relates to the manner in which he supported his balancing pole. Did the pole appear to be near to or far from his body?"

"Near to?" I answer, wondering what Tom is getting at.

"Correct, Billy—and an excellent illustration of the basic principle of *connection*, as important in golf as it is in tightrope walking." Tom points his thumbs to his underarms. "An overt pressure exists between the tightrope walker's upper arms and upper rib cage, while his forearms will remain quite passive. This pressure ensures proper connection of *the balancing pole* to his body. A similar pressure connects *the golf club* to the body of a golfer. The two become one—in each pursuit."

I'm confused. "I thought you said the hands were the body's connection to the golf club?" I query.

"A perfect question, Billy! You have been paying attention. Your are becoming a healthy thinker." Tom's excitement eases my frustration at this apparent paradox. "The hands are the body's *physical* connection to the golf club, whereas the upper arms are the body's *functional* connection to the club. Be very clear of the difference, Billy. Rest assured, we will talk more about the term *connection* at a later time."

"I think I understand," I say.

I wonder if my golf swing has ever truly had proper connection. I know it hasn't. My arms go wherever they choose. My body goes wherever it chooses. How have I had *any* success in this sport? I feel now as if I knew nothing before about the golf swing.

Tom stops my self-interrogation. "What can you tell me about the balance displayed by the acrobats, the clowns on the unicycles and the woman standing on the running elephants?"

"Not much, Tom," I return dismissively. "I wasn't really paying attention."

"Too bad," Tom replies. "Many natural truths were clearly in front of you. You were here, but you weren't really *here*— until I asked you to be." Tom nods in the direction of the circus ring below. "To fully experience the present moment is to experience life, Billy. Wait no longer to discover this truth. When your mind was left alone to observe the circus, your illusions of a dreamed up past and future replaced your true experience. You were daydreaming!" he concludes in semi-mockery. "Strive to be present, Billy—as present as you were when observing the tightrope walker."

My depth and Tom's depth are clearly in different swimming pools.

I did experience the tightrope walker much more completely, though—which I enjoyed. Is it possible to be *that* present all of the time?

Tom could tell I was feeling overwhelmed. "Don't fret, Billy," he comforts. "Your skills of presence will improve as you continue to gain knowledge, apply it and review." He abruptly takes on a brooding focus. **"No tool is more important—whether in golf, health or life—than** *presence*."

Tom allows me a few moments to write down and reflect on this significant message.

From the corner of my eye, I notice him quietly take in a deep breath, hold it for a several seconds and then exhale fully. He repeats this exercise several times and then addresses me again.

"Seek counsel from your CPGA professional about balance—including pace, rhythm, posture, spinal angle and connection. Apply this knowledge as habit. Challenge yourself to make practice swings under the most difficult of balance situations. Swing in bare feet or with your eyes closed. Try to make swings in your slowest slow motion. Swing a weighted club. Hit shots with your feet together. Observe the response of your body's natural balance mechanisms in each of these modes of practice."

Tom sips his water and then pauses suddenly. "Do you like football, Billy?"

"Yeah—sure—why?" I chuckle.

"Next meeting, we will really go to school for an important golf lesson—your school!"

As usual, Tom catches me off guard. As usual, I stare blankly.

"Meet me in Coach Bloom's room at Crescent Heights High School at 3:20 on Friday afternoon. We will be there for just over one hour," he says. "It will be a golf lesson you will never forget."

We return to our seats, where Tom sits in balance and—for once—so do I.

Here, in the last row of the darkened Medicine Hat Arena, range picker Tom Morrison and I drink water and experience the simplicity, balance and skill of the rest of the circus performers.

Chapter 9

Bloom's Room

I'm busy packing my books into my locker Friday afternoon, as I've just finished my last class for the day. It's strange knowing that Old Tom is at my school. Outsiders rarely roam the Crescent Heights High School hallways, let alone golf course range pickers. But Tom Morrison is not your ordinary range picker. And he has made me question the need to *be ordinary*.

I arrive at the office of CHHS gym teacher and football coach, Jim Bloom, just before 3:20. Tom answers my knock immediately, holding two large bottles of water. "Good day, Billy. Come in. Have a seat."

I smile and enter.

He gestures toward a seat in front of a videotape machine and hands me one of the water bottles. "I want to go through some video tapes with you. Coach Bloom has been kind enough to let us use his room—to study some game films."

Game films? What the heck is the old timer up to this time? I settle in without question. Each road trip so far has been entertaining *and* informative. Why should this be any different?

He pushes the start button on the video machine, sits erect, yet comfortably, and speaks matter-of-factly. "Tell me what you see, Billy."

The tape begins to run, showing a football play. More specifically, it shows a handoff to a running back, who is tackled near the line of scrimmage, or for what looks to be a gain of a yard, maybe two. The scene seems pretty obvious, but I'm no football analyst.

"I see a football play where the running back gets the ball from the quarterback and gains about a yard. Second down and nine to go." I'm reasonably proud of my answer.

Tom calmly turns to me. "That is what most everyone would see, Billy. Look deeper. Put yourself in Coach Bloom's shoes. Ask yourself what he sees when he reviews this tape. Is the play successful? If so, what makes it successful? If not, what went wrong? What is the team trying to accomplish by running this play? What is their plan?"

I'm a golfer, not a football coach, is my first thought. Yet, I trust that Tom is taking me somewhere important. I pull my chair closer and watch the play again, looking deeper. I soon realize that the play didn't come off as planned.

"It's a broken play," I say triumphantly. "The running back gets to the line of scrimmage and has nowhere to go. He changes direction and makes something out of nothing. He gains a yard on the play. He never gives up. Coach Bloom would be impressed with his effort."

There—I've nailed it! It's the running back's effort that Tom wants me to notice. Just like what he probably expects from me on the golf course—in a tough situation, stick in there and make the most of it. *Perseverance* is the message!

"Good, Billy," Tom smiles. There is a new gleam in his eye. "You are starting to see universal lessons. And they *are* everywhere. The running back makes the best of a bad situation, true. A prevalent theme in golf and also in life." He pauses. "Unfortunately, it is not what I brought you here to see. We are looking for the fourth cornerstone of the golf swing."

The golf swing?

"Watch this next play." Without hesitation, Tom leans over, fast-forwards the videotape and hits the play button. "Tell me what you see this time."

Once again, the running back takes the handoff from the quarterback. This time, there is an opening at the line of scrimmage. He runs through the line of scrimmage easily and is soon tackled. He looks to have gained five yards on the play.

I hesitate, embarrassed to state the obvious. "The play is successful this time. The offensive linemen have more time to open up a hole at the line of scrimmage and the running back gains five yards. Second down and five to go." My tone is a question as much as an answer.

Tom looks at me as if I should have more to say. Unfortunately, that's it. We stare at each other for a few seconds.

"Look deeper," he finally emphasizes with a loud whisper. "Why did the second play work better than the first? You're close."

I'm drawn in by his tone.

"There's a hole at the line of scrimmage on the second play," I say.

"Why?" Tom whispers, as he squints and leans toward me.

"The offensive linemen open it up—by blocking the other team's linemen," I reply hesitantly.

"Excellent! You are realizing that there is several individual actions within one simple-looking hand-off play," Tom says. "Why didn't the linemen open up a hole on the first play?"

"I don't—know," I stammer. "Although they didn't seem to have as much *time* on the first play. The running back seemed to get there too quickly, before anything had developed."

"Excellent." Tom calmly fast-forwards the tape to another part of the game and hits the play button. "Tell me what you see now."

His actions remain methodical despite his progress, like a lion patiently approaching prey. I watch the next play as I have never watched a football play before in my life. I feel like I *am* Coach Bloom.

The running back receives the handoff from the quarterback again. Again, there is a big hole at the line of scrimmage. This time, it seems as if there is no defense. The running back runs for fifteen yards before finally being tackled.

"Wow!" I blurt reflexively. "What a great play! This time the running back had free sailing through the defensive line *and* through the defensive secondary. I don't know why it happened, but it looked free and easy—almost effortless. It was nice to watch!"

"Way to go, kid!" Tom barks. "Now you're getting somewhere. Watch all three plays again a few times and tell me what you see."

Tom rewinds the same three high school football plays over and over for the remainder of the hour. They are no different than plays I've seen a hundred times at high school football games and on TV. Now I'm watching them as if watching man first walk on the moon.

Tom hits the stop button for a final time. "Tell me everything you saw, Billy."

I am still unclear of the answer he wants, but I have a good sense of what I have seen. I feel more confident as an independent thinker.

"On the first play," I begin my analysis, "the team is out of sync and the play does not come off successfully. The second play looks better—smoother. The third play is best of all and seems to work with great ease. All motions appear to be one motion. I don't know enough about football to say why. Each play just seems less rushed and in better order than the previous."

I can tell Tom is satisfied with my effort.

"You are very correct in your observations, Billy. You are beginning to learn the importance of *sequence. All motions appear to be one motion*—I like that. May I use this phrase in future guides?"

Tom wants to use *my* phrase?

"Sure, Tom," I wisecrack. " I guess I've picked up a line or two from you in exchange."

"Sequence is as important in the golf swing as it is in these football plays." Tom remains in guide mode, again without any reaction to my obvious wit. "The only difference is that, in golf, there is no opposition, no reason for impatience." Tom rises and approaches the chalkboard as if *he* is now the head football coach of the CHHS Vikings. "For this simple hand-off play to be successful, an entire sequence of seemingly separate events must occur as one. 'All motions appear to be one motion'."

I blush proudly.

"Sequence must occur rhythmically in order, neither too quickly nor too slowly," he says as he begins to diagram the play on the chalkboard. "First, the *center* snaps the football to the *quarterback*. Next, the two offensive backs begin their motion. The first back, the *fullback*, begins to move to provide blocking for the second back, the *halfback*. The halfback receives the football from the quarterback. Meanwhile, the offensive *linemen* have begun to block the other team's defensive linemen to provide a hole for the fullback and the halfback to run through. They both run through this hole at the line of scrimmage. The fullback then blocks the other team's next player, the defensive *linebacker*. This opens a hole in the defensive secondary for the halfback to run through easily. A thing of beauty—*in the correct sequence*."

I sit mildly bewildered by the football references, yet I can see easily what he is getting at. And I know enough about the golf swing to take a stab at the golf cornerstone Tom is showing me.

I stand up, hook my hands together as if gripping a golf club and assume my golf stance. "So what you're saying is that if my swing is in proper sequence, it will seem easy to hit the ball, just like the ease of the proper football play." I pause in reflection. "Tom, I've felt this before when things are going well on the golf course—it's as if the motion just flows naturally in one piece. But when things are going poorly, I feel like my body isn't moving together at all. My timing feels off. I feel jerky and uncomfortable."

Tom nods. "You've got the idea, Billy. Most physical endeavours appear easy when sequence is orchestrated properly—like the successful football play. When the individual steps occur too early or too late, success is unlikely. You'll better understand golf swing sequence when we next meet."

Just as Tom finishes his comment, Coach Bloom walks into the room. Our lesson ends perfectly on time.

Coach Bloom glances passively at me from overtop of his clipboard. "Are you ready to explain *sequence* to my football team next season, Billy?"

I'm not the first to receive Tom's *guidance* in here.

"Not yet, Coach," I say. "I'd better explain it to myself, first."

Tom rises from his chair. "Thank you for the use of your room, Coach. See you next time."

"Anytime, Tommy," Coach Bloom returns and then addresses me again. "You must be a pretty special player for Tom to have you in here."

I nod. "Pretty lucky is more like it." My comment is an attempt to indirectly compliment Tom.

Tom remains humble as we walk out of Coach Bloom's office—his stride and posture are unchanged. I'm sure he senses how impressed I am with him and his guiding lessons, but adulation from others just doesn't seem to make any difference to him.

"See you on the driving range at 5 pm on Saturday, Billy. I will require two and a half hours of your time," is all he says in parting.

Chapter 10

The Setting Sun

I arrive at the driving range twenty minutes early on Saturday. I take a seat beside Tom's chair and watch him out on the range. At the foot of his chair, I notice a bucket of soapy water, a brush and a towel.

Tom is on the far side of the range chipping range balls away from the fence. This is the first time I've seen him hit a golf ball. His hands appear extremely soft on the club. Each shot seems identical. Each is hit with noticeable simplicity and ease of motion.

I think of how quickly these weeks have passed and how dramatically my thought process has changed and grown. I smile thankfully for having a chance to meet this man so kind-hearted, helpful and giving—and so wise. I sense that this might be our last lesson together, having only the last golf cornerstone to cover. Tonight might be it for Tom and I as "guide and pupil." I feel a certain sadness.

I am reminded again of a time not long ago when I would have felt silly hanging out with Old Tom Morrison, the range picker. I think of how much I would have missed had I followed Gus Geraldi's fear-rooted advice. I think of how my perception of each man has changed. I can't wait for Tom's lessons now. He has become like a parent or a best friend to me as much as a teacher—check that, *guide*. Time spent with him is valuable, worthwhile, inspiring. He makes me want to excel in every way—and to maybe even help others someday, as he has helped me. I feel like telling everyone about him. My ego wouldn't have allowed me to think this way two short weeks ago. Two short weeks ago, I didn't even know I *had* an ego!

"On time again—early, in fact," Tom snaps cheerfully. "Good boy, Billy." Tom has a way of moving without making noise. "Let's get started," he says. "Today's lesson is very important."

Tom immerses his 7-iron into the bucket of soapy water and then bends forward with fanned knees to brush the grooves of the iron clean. In smooth progression, he scrubs the handle and towels dry the entire club.

"Take good care of your clubs, Billy," he winks, "and they will take good care of you."

"Is that the lesson today, Tom? The fourth cornerstone of the golf swing—keep your clubs clean!" More skillful comedy from the kid from The Hat!

As usual, no reaction from my one-man audience. Instead, Tom's face takes on a focus that I have come to recognize and respect, like theatre lights dimming for a performance.

"*Sequence* is the fourth and final golf swing cornerstone." Tom's motions are smooth and deliberate. "Like the successful football play, all separate golf swing actions take place as one in an efficient, logical sequence. You can have an excellent grip, flawless alignment and balanced posture, and yet the ball remains at rest until the body and club are put into motion."

"I've never heard anyone talk about *sequence* before, Tom," I interrupt.

"You have, Billy, but in different terms," Tom counters. "Terms like 'connection,' 'large muscles swing the club,' 'lead with the legs,' and 'club in front of the body' are all sequence terms."

Tom and his newly cleaned 7-iron move a few yards ahead, where a small plastic range basket houses ten or so range balls. Tom knocks over the basket with his club head to access the balls. He looks back and winks. "Today's lesson you must never forget."

Instant excitement! Is the old man about to hit some shots? Can he really play? Does he actually have some game? Theory is one thing in golf, sure, but application—that's a whole different animal!

Tom uses his iron to coral a ball from the small pile. He rolls it to a flat spot on the grass in front of him. His movements are now more rhythmic and natural than ever. He speaks with clarity. "The proper golf swing sequence gives you power, accuracy and consistency. Let's talk first about the loading action of the swing, the backswing. You would do well to take notes, Billy."

I have unknowingly morphed from *student* into *groupie*. Tom waits as I fumble for my pen and pad. "Ready" I nod.

"The backswing requires the upper body to turn away from the target against the resistance and stability of the lower body. The lower body provides the foundation for all shots. The stable lower body connects the golfer to the ground, and the upper body to the lower body. The shoulders rotate fully, the hips minimally in comparison. The spine angle remains unchanged. The spinal curves are supported. The chin is level. Recall the tightrope walker's *connection* of his body to the balancing pole. The same connection of golfer to golf club ensures that the golfer's torso and club move together, in sequence.

"Can you clarify *connection* again, Tom—in golf terms?" I ask. I am still marred in *connection confusion*.

"I can do one better," Tom says with a smile. "I can show you a drill that many tour players use to train the functional connection of club to body."

Tom reaches into both his front pockets and yanks a golf glove from each. "This question often comes up." He proceeds to stuff one glove under each armpit. "Many tour players hit practice shots holding golf gloves in this manner. Hold the gloves as long as possible, reminding the body and club to move as one—*in connection*. A golfer who is a beginner or is physically weak or who lacks flexibility will find this drill to be difficult. These golfers may be lenient and allow the arms to wander somewhat."

"You saw this drill on TV?" I dig for information.

"In person, Billy," Tom replies casually, then continues his explanation. "You may also hear *connection* used in reference to the stable foundation—the golfer's connection to the ground. Or you may hear *connection* used in reference to the loaded coil sensation—the golfer's connection of the upper body to the lower body. Do not confuse the references."

I'm glad I asked. Connection has always been a bit blurry to me. And I notice he cleverly avoided my question about tour players. He isn't about to make any lesson about himself. I can tell he has tons of golf history hidden inside him. Does he really guide touring pros?

"The two end products of the proper backswing are balance and stored power—the loaded coil sensation. Ensure that you complete your backswing fully, in a controlled manner, maintaining a stable base—maintaining your spinal curves. There is no need to rush the backswing or to rush into the downswing. The backswing sets the rhythm for all shots. The final backswing position is a strong predictor of the shot to follow."

Tom sets up to the range ball. He bends his knees slightly and tilts his torso forward from the hip joints. His arms hang naturally. The club appears stable in his hands. Maintaining his signature flawless posture, he turns his upper body fully against the resistance of his stable lower body, underarm gloves in place and all. Man, he looks solid! "Have your CPGA teaching professional ensure that you are in a stable, coiled and connected position at the top of your backswing. It is a most important position—a position that most golfers rush through in a blur."

Tom easily maintains this backswing position and speaks candidly.

"The body unloads this loaded coil during the downswing, the main part of sequence. From here forward, the best players in the world look very similar. All actions continue to occur in connection, as one. Maximum power, accuracy and consistency are the result. The spine angle remains the same throughout the action to the balanced finish. The hands remain passive. 'Give up control to gain control.' That's what Knudson used to say."

Wow—Knudson! George Knudson is a famous Canadian professional who passed away in 1989. Knudson won eight times on the PGA tour in the '60s and early '70s. He won back to back in Phoenix and Tucson and won the World Cup for Canada partnered with Al Balding, in 1968. Then he finished second in the Masters in 1969. I've read about him and seen his swing on film. Knudson had an immaculate golf swing.

Tom knew Knudson? Tom played with him? I'm becoming more curious by the second.

"You knew Knudson?" I blurt.

Tom looks at me impatiently. "Here comes the main part of sequence, Billy: *pay attention.* Just like the football play, the club head must arrive on time. It moves as one, in connection with the turning motion of the balanced body."

He speaks deliberately as he moves in majestic slow motion:

"The legs and hips begin the swing sequence down the power line. The left hip rotates fully through to lead the body. The torso turns with the turning motion of the hips, the shoulders turn with the torso, the arms follow the shoulders in connection and the hands follow the arms, delivering the club head through the ball down the target

line. The club head follows the motion of the body. The entire motion occurs as one."

"The spine angle remains constant during the swing action through to a balanced finish. The spinal curves are always supported. The chin is level. The hands are passive. The motion produces a rhythmic sweep—not a hit—down and through the ball towards the target."

"Do this properly and a full, balanced finish position facing the target occurs naturally. Hold your finish as a final check of proper balance and sequence."

Tom looks back at me as if disarming wired dynamite. "There is no reason to rush the swing. When the football play was rushed, the sequence was crowded. The play could still occur, but the chance of success was greatly reduced."

"The halfback arrived at the line of scrimmage in poor sequence," I say.

"Correct," Tom nods. "In golf, there is no opposition, save for the player's own dreamed-up fears of *past* and *future*. Fear is non-existent—*when one is truly present*."

Why do I occasionally get so mortified facing a simple golf shot? It's not like any lives are at stake during a tee shot. The sun will still rise the next day regardless of the outcome of a putt. Tom's reminder of *presence* excites me.

I still need to clarify what Tom means by *rush*. "Aren't some people just naturally fast?" I ask.

"Good question, Billy. Maybe you will be fortunate enough to teach golf yourself one day. You change people's lives when you teach them golf."

He pauses, assuring that I will fully digest his comment. I digest and smile.

He continues. "Whatever a golfer's natural way, fast or slow, the golf swing must be *rhythmic*. This may appear quite different from one golfer to another, as rhythm is an individual trait. If I tell students that some people are naturally fast and some are naturally slow, it gives them carte blanche to swing without rhythm. Think in terms of *rhythm*, Billy, not in terms of fast or slow."

Tom puts one finger up. "Poor rhythm of sequence is one sure way to ruin the golf swing."

Tom puts two fingers up. "Poor order of sequence is another. Many golfers hold the club in a death grip, a dire mistake. Few shots ever call for a firm grip, deep rough being one example. Unwarranted grip pressure can cause the player to activate the hands—not the body—to initiate the shot, ruining swing sequence. The hands do very little consciously in the golf swing. They react. They follow the body's lead. The hands deliver the club head passively, in sequence—and remember to keep your grips clean so that light grip pressure is possible."

"The halfback is the club head, right?" I ask in a moment of Zen.

"Yes. Both are the last to arrive. Like the halfback, the club head must arrive on time. Too early usually reveals poor sequence. Too late usually reveals poor connection of club to body."

Tom turns and approaches the awaiting range ball. He attentively sets his club head down the target line and tactfully takes his grip. Next, he sets his feet, hips and shoulders on the power line and adjusts his posture. He tilts his torso forward slightly from the hip sockets, creating his spinal angle. I observe a slight forward hollow in his lower back, a stable butt position and a bit of knee flex. His chin is level. Rhythmically and athletically, he turns his upper body fully against the resistance of his lower body, creating a coiled, energetic position at the top of his backswing. There appears to be a minute pause to complete his coil, after which he drives his body down the power line. His legs and hips initiate the motion. His left hip rotates fully and initiates the turning action of the rest of the body. Body and club move as one, in sequence. His hands appear passive. His motion appears effortless. The contact of clubface to ball makes a crisp crack, the likes of which I have never heard. His spinal angle and chin position remain solid through the swing to a balanced finish. The ball flies dead straight and lands softly in the distance.

He turns partially to address me. "Grip, alignment, balance and sequence on every shot, Billy. Learn them, apply them and review them regularly."

Tom repeats the same process to hit another ball. Another ball explodes off his iron face, again flying dead straight and landing softly.

"Grip, alignment, balance and sequence on every shot. Learn them, apply them and review them regularly."

One shot after another is identical until no range balls remain.

I sit stunned, jaw hanging.

Tom's mood is unaffected by my guise of hero worship, as if to display to me that the four cornerstones of the golf swing have hit these terrific golf shots, not him.

"The more you master these four cornerstones on every shot, the more you will advance in this game," he says.

Tom whistles as he walks back to the soapy water bucket, contently scrubs and dries his club and takes his seat. Without even the hint of a closing ceremony, his sequence lesson is over.

*

We continue to talk quietly on the driving range that Saturday night, combing briefly over the lessons I have learned thus far. At no time do we speak about Tom.

Soon, he shifts his sitting position and looks down the driving range, appearing deep in thought. "If sequence ties everything together in golf, what then does the same in health? What fourth cornerstone must all humans have to survive?"

During the time of Tom's lessons, I feel like I've successfully expanded my health awareness—maybe as much as I have my golf swing knowledge. I have become conscious of my breathing. I've been eating a variety of fresh fruits and vegetables daily, drinking lots of water and exercising regularly, indoors and out. I've even taken my parents, Danny and Leah to Redcliff to meet Jerry Colter. So I welcome the challenge of Tom's riddle and begin to think out loud.

"Food, water, air and—" I hesitate. What can the fourth be? "If I have food, water and air available to me, what else could there be? What else do I need? I can't think of anything, Tom. Is this a trick question? Are there only three health cornerstones?"

"There are four," Tom assures me. "Compare the fourth golf cornerstone. It is an appropriate hint."

"Sequence—" I say, "Sequence sets the other *golf* cornerstones in motion. What sets the first three *health* cornerstones in motion? I'm drawing a blank, Tom."

"Do you know what a *cadaver* is, Billy?" Tom asks immediately.

"It's a dead person, right?" I know this one. "I remember seeing cadavers in one of my favourite movies, Drop Dead Gorgeous. Kirsten Dunst plays a character who is a make-up artist in a funeral home."

"Close enough, Billy. A dead body is generally referred as a *corpse* or a *body*, whereas a *cadaver* is a body prepared specifically for study." Tom clears the definition without emotion. "Regardless, each example applies. If an endless supply of food, water and oxygen are available to a corpse or a cadaver, what happens?"

"That's a gruesome example, Tom," I chuckle.

"What happens?" he insists.

He's still all business.

"Nothing happens. Cadavers and corpses are both dead." I say.

"So we agree that food, water and oxygen are not the only health necessities," Tom returns.

"Yeah, I guess—" I nod weakly.

"What then do both the cadaver and the corpse lack?"

"A heartbeat for one," I quip in half-laugh. To my surprise, my off-hand comment draws Tom in closer.

"And what makes the heart beat?" he murmurs keenly.

"Signals—" I start and pause.

"From where?"

"From—the brain—I think?"

"And what body system is the brain part of?" Tom queries.

"The—nervous system?" I'm out of my league now.

"Exactly right!" Tom growls victoriously. "Exactly right, kid!"

"I am?" I say in disbelief. I *am* learning something in biology class after all!

"The forth cornerstone of health—*a healthy nervous system*," Tom states robustly. "The brain and the network of nerves make up the nervous system. The nervous system controls, stores and monitors every memory, thought, sensation and action. It is the first system to emerge in a developing human, the system that orchestrates the *building* of the entire body—from *two single cells* into *tens of trillions, nonetheless*. Once developed, it detects and reacts to invaders, tells the heart to beat, the skin to repair, the lungs to breathe, the intestines to absorb food—I could go on and on. Every single process in the body is monitored and organized by the boundless nervous system, 365 days a year, 24/7. Indeed, it is a system remarkable beyond explanation—more remarkable by far than the smartest computer. And yet, most of us take it completely for granted and treat it poorly."

I must look like the cliché deer caught in the headlights. This *healthy nervous system* stuff is all news to me.

Tom once again appears deep in thought. "You can see that there is no electrical plug-in for this magnificent nervous system, yet it works every day around the clock. What then is it that instructs the nervous system to function, Billy?"

I laugh in surrender. "I have no idea, Tom. I think I've already pulled the last trick from my trivia bag."

"Take a guess, Billy," Tom prods, challenging me to widen my boundaries even further. "You are much wiser than you are aware."

I've never thought about what runs the nervous system. It just runs! "It's just nature, isn't it?" I speculate.

"A darn good guess, Billy!" He nods intently. "Indeed, this is a question that has intrigued philosophers since the beginning of human existence, a question that has started many wars. What do we call *That* which supplies life; *That* which instructs the nervous system in design, function and maintenance; *That* which animates the living world? Is it God? Nature? Spirit? Innate Intelligence? Consciousness? Which one is it?"

Nothing from me. Silence. Whoa—this conversation is now officially above my head.

Tom bails me out. "All must be equally correct and are, in fact, of one and the same. There can only be one *Source* of life, regardless of the label one prefers." He smiles appreciatively. "Regardless of individual beliefs, this *It* is an intelligence beyond the comprehension of the human mind. *It* is an intelligence that cannot be defined or duplicated, only sensed. *It* builds fully functional, coordinated life forms! The miraculous

It is inside all living things, making *all life equal*—the simplest truth of all. When we discover and are fully humbled by the truth of our own enormity, we are free to discover the true path of inspiration and contentment. *All* is already within, Billy—a cause for celebration." Tom remains serene and then chuckles loudly, perhaps in mockery of my perplexed gawk. "Maybe you weren't aware of the true nature of your greatness, Billy."

I shake my head *very slowly*.

He settles back, as if to re-involve me in the conversation. "Tell me some ways to maximize your nervous system health."

This is certainly a lot for me to process and Tom knows it. I don't give up. I'm inspired to challenge myself and follow his train of thought. Maybe I am wiser than I think. Is it really possible that *God might be inside me, helping me to do things*?

"Sleep must be one!" I bark. How did that come to me?

"Good, Billy. Proper sleep is a key contributor to a maximally healthy nervous system. Not too little, not too much. Six to eight hours per night for most. What else?"

"Humour?" I say. "That must be one. I always seem to feel better when I laugh a lot."

"Right on, kid. Humour is essential. Mark Twain wrote: 'Against the assault of laughter nothing can stand.' The American poet, E. E. Cummings wrote: 'The most wasted of all days is one without laughter.' To laugh is to live, a most necessary tool for a healthy nervous system. Keep going, Billy. You are rolling."

"I've always sensed that hitting golf balls makes me relax and feel clear. My problems just seem to go away. Could that be one?" I *am* rolling!

"Passion—absolutely necessary for maximum nervous system wellness and vitality. Pursue that which you are passionate for. Listen deeply to your Inside Voice for guidance, Billy. Passion is a most basic healthy nervous system stimulant.

You are very correct. What else do you know about a healthy nervous system? We have recently touched on it."

I twitch my shoulders and eyebrows in unison and shake my head. "There's more to a healthy nervous system?"

"Much more. It is quite possibly an infinite subject," Tom says and then shifts back towards me. "Remember posture and balance, Billy?" he asks rhetorically. "The delicate nervous system is protected by the skull and the spine, making spinal balance one of the most vital basic health considerations of all—and one of the most overlooked!" He smiles, as if in awe. "Nerves continually communicate healthy messages back and . forth between the brain and the tissues of the body. The nervous system is constantly evaluating and reacting to the body's absolute needs. A balanced spine permits uninterrupted nervous system communication within the body, creating harmony— called *homeostasis*. Spinal imbalance, on the other hand, challenges this harmony."

My blank stare is interrupted by Tom's stern gesture for me to take notes.

He tilts his head and shoulders and contorts his pelvis into a position of bad posture. "Spinal posture is as important to the *nervous system* cornerstone of health as it is to the *balance* cornerstone of golf. Observe head tilt and shoulder and hip levels in yourself and others. You will become well aware of the abundant amount of ill-health and energy waste within our population; a true shame."

Tom allows his head, shoulders and pelvis to readjust to normal, seemingly dead level. "The better the spine, the better the nervous system potential, Billy. Explore the spinal balance specialties of chiropractic care, massage therapy and exercise therapy. Explore Pilates, Yoga, swimming and regular stretching, for starters. Continue to learn about proper sitting, standing, and sleeping postures. When the spine is truly balanced, health potential becomes limitless."

I continue to laboriously scribble out notes.

Tom continues to smile comfortably. "What are you thinking *right now*?" he asks.

"I'm thinking that my brain is full and that I don't know very much about my own body," I say casually.

His focus remains constant, his voice calm. "*Thought* is the food of the human nervous system, Billy. Make note of this now and remember it always: *your thoughts form your reality.* Most humans have the absolute freedom to choose their thoughts. Take close care to think healthy thoughts." Tom pauses apathetically. "Positivity breeds success and ease. Negativity breeds failure and dis-ease. Most *feed* negativity and cynicism to themselves—and to others."

Tom appears detached from his comments, as if these *truths* of which he speaks are common knowledge.

"Or maybe I'm just not as smart as you give me credit for," I say, half-jokingly.

My clowning doesn't temper Tom's focus.

"You built yourself from two cells, Billy. Rest assured, you have no shortage of intelligence within you. Your intelligence is limitless. You are *not as smart as I give you credit for*, as you say, only because you have agreed to think so," he says. "Negativity *is* unnatural and *is* a choice, always past and future orientated, always created by the fearful ego. When the mind operates as ego, the body's wondrous wisdom is silenced—held hostage." He picks up his 7-iron and begins to admire it. "The mind cannot exist as ego in the present. In the present moment, the mind is what it truly is—*a tool* that serves the body—just as a leg or an arm or a nose is a tool. It is an observer, an evaluator and a problem solver. It does not judge, fear nor hinder the wisdom of your nature. It *thinks* only in terms of cooperation and service. In the present, you are free to be *you*. And as you begin to truly understand *you*, you will see that there is no end to your intelligence—or your health—or your skill."

These comments are a little too *joyous* for me to accept. "I doubt I can be positive all the time, Tom. Like, what about when I get bad bounces on the golf course, for example?"

Tom laughs instantly. "Rest assured, Billy, unbiased universal laws are already well in place, determining all happenings. What any golfer refers to as a 'bad bounce' is a deficiency in his or her skill or character—or is nothing at all. The Roman philosopher Cicero wrote: 'The absolute good is not a matter of opinion, but of nature.' We are each but tiny players in a vast reality. How vast, who is to say? What is important is that *how each tiny player reacts to each tiny happening determines a new vast reality*." Tom's smile flattens a bit and the rhythm of his speech slows. "Strive to keep your mind present and constructive, free for higher observation. It serves no purpose to be conflicted by *what is,* Billy. Be patient when observing life's messages. Conflict with *what is* is known as *stress,* the greatest deterrent of all to nervous system health. Accept *what is*, process *what is*, and then act immediately and constructively, if action is necessary. You will develop great character. You will learn and grow and find peace."

Tom's perspective leaves me perplexed and silent.

He suddenly becomes giddy, as if explaining a riddle. "The essence of one's thoughts *and* actions are central to one's nervous system health. To be positive and caring aligns us with our deepest nature. Millman, the American gymnastic champion and spiritual teacher, wrote 'Kindness completes our lives.' Thomas Merton, the French-born spiritual master and monk, wrote: 'If you have love, you will do all things well.' A nervous system unfrightened by negativity performs miracles." Tom chuckles. "Consider the word 'fright', Billy, and this appropriate word play:

When the 'f' from fear
Is removed from fright,
What is *left*
Is what is *right*

"Remove fear and negativity from the nervous system. Accomplish this by *being present* in each moment. What remains is unlimited wisdom, healing and performance potential—*what is right.* Your health and your performance— and the rest of the world— will celebrate!"

Though barely hanging on in the conversation, I am intrigued. I often sense "fear" inside myself without any idea of why it's there. I'm starting to sense that it serves no purpose. It just holds me back.

"Seek counsel from the spiritual authors like Tolle, Dyer, Millman, Robbins, Krishnamurti and DeMartini. Connect your Infinite with your finite. It is a most rewarding relationship."

"This all sounds pretty complicated, Tom," I plead.

"In fact, Billy, it is the easiest," he smiles. "Be present in all you do. Sense your nature. Experience each moment, *big* or *small*—love, laugh, cry, smile, touch, smell, taste, hear, see, camp, fish, watch a movie, dance, walk in the rain, volunteer, read, teach, learn, exercise, meditate, write, sing, build, explore, cook, paint, hug, create, play cards, invent, bowl, wash dishes by hand, pray, ride a horse, whistle, smell a flower, hike, study your city's history, donate, garden, travel, listen to music, make music, play with a pet, learn your family tree, draw, craft, plan a surprise, contact an old friend, do a jigsaw puzzle, have a picnic, play a game. Take your pick, Billy—whatever you are doing—*live!*" Tom pauses, enjoying the silence, then gazes mystically. "You have gained a most precious prospective this evening for acheiving *ease* in health and life—and also in golf."

I smile in awe. Tom is so peaceful when he speaks, yet so decisive and passionate. I've never heard such ideas, though

I've always sensed a relationship between negativity and poor play.

Who is this guy? He doesn't seem to care at all what I think of him—or what anybody thinks of him, for that matter. He just *guides* unselfishly. He's humble yet individual, plain yet wise. And never seems to tire. Being around Tom has moved me dramatically, though he seems so simple. Maybe that's the point.

"We will meet once more, Billy," Tom says. "Tomorrow night at 6. This time, please come to my home for dinner. I would like you to meet my wife, Thelma. She is a wonderful person. I am blessed." He hesitates. "Do you have a girlfriend?"

"Yes," I say proudly. "Her name is Leah."

"Please bring Leah, if she is able." Tom hands me a neatly folded piece of paper. "I have taken the liberty to write down our address. Be prepared with any questions that remain. I will answer all that are important."

"Thanks, Tom," I say graciously. "'Sounds like fun—we'll be there."

We continue to sit together on the driving range and marvel at the strength and beauty of the setting sun.

Chapter 11

The Morrison's

I wait in the living room of Leah's parents house, Lois and Brent Bremont. Mr. Bremont is Leah's stepfather. Leah's parents split up when she was eight. Leah's Dad is still active in her life. I've met him twice—he seems like a pretty good guy. Both Leah and Robin, her younger sister by one year, are well adapted to their *situation*.

I've been so involved with Tom lately that I've cancelled a few dates with Leah. It's the source of some recent arguing between us. Yet again, she's been forced to play second fiddle to my golf. Leah's not the type of girl that needs to play second fiddle to anything—or anyone. I don't like when we argue, but I have a career to pursue. It's difficult to keep the two—golf and romance—balanced.

"Hi, Billy." Mrs. Bremont peeks into the living room. "Where have you been lately? We've missed you these last few Wednesdays."

Leah's Mom makes a killer roast beef dinner most Wednesday nights. And most Wednesday nights, I act as the house garburator. But my garburator reputation is certain to be hurt by my new *nibble* versus *gorge* approach to eating, as recommended by Jerry Colter.

"I've been busy with a new golf coach," I say. "Leah and I are going to his house for dinner tonight. I'm excited for Leah to meet Old Tom."

"I hope he's worth it. You've missed some of my best work."

"Yeah, I'm learning lots, Mrs. B. More than I thought was possible in such a short time. My Wednesday's are freeing up soon, though. I'm ready to get back in the rotation—if you'll have me."

"Yeah, we'll take you back in." Mrs. Bremont winks." Leah should be down in a few minutes. Have fun tonight."

"Thanks."

I really like Mrs. Bremont. She has a great sense of humour and always treats me well. I sense that she likes me for her daughter, though she's fully aware of how golf-focused I can be. She knows it gets in the way of Leah and I sometimes. It's about the only thing that does. I am very much in love with Leah and wish I didn't have to choose between my time with her and my time with golf.

Leah's footsteps stir me from my thoughts. I watch her as she walks down the stairs, realizing I haven't seen her in a full week. She looks beautiful—I forgot just how beautiful she is.

"Hi, Billy," she says softly.

"Hi, Leah," I return, shaking my head slowly. "You look incredible."

Leah is tall and slim with darkish auburn hair and hazel eyes. She's wearing capri-style blue jeans, leather sandals and a long sleeved white blouse with a collar and string tie-ups at the wrists. She has a classy, carefree walk I have grown to love. I welcome her with a tight hug at the bottom of the stairs.

"I've missed you, Billy," she says and then smiles casually. "I'm looking forward to meeting my competition tonight."

Leah has her Mom's sense of humour. I feel at ease immediately as she makes light of our recent *bone of contention.*

"Don't worry, Leah. You're a ton cuter than he is."

"Good," she says playfully. "Maybe I'll have you back all to myself one of these days."

Just then, a deep sense of sincerity runs through me. "I'm really glad you could make it tonight, Leah. Tom has made a big impact on me. I want you to know him. His lessons have made me a different person—a better person. I can feel it."

"I thought he's teaching you golf?" Leah says, wrinkling her face.

"He is," I say. "It's just that golf is much more than I thought—and much less—it's hard to explain—I just want you to meet him."

Leah processes my clumsy comment for a moment. "If you can't beat 'em, join 'em."

*

The doorbell echoes inside the Morrison house. A pleasant older woman greets us at the door.

"You must be Billy and Leah," she smiles warmly. "I am Thelma Morrison. Please call me Thelma. Welcome."

Leah and I exchange pleasantries with Thelma as we make our way inside.

"Tom is in the sitting room having tea," she says. "Please come and sit with us."

Thelma is striking in appearance. Her frame presents as thin and lean, yet strong. Indeed, she is much taller than Tom. Though her hair is completely grayed, her skin is youthful and healthy. Her posture is excellent and comfortable, like Tom's.

Her actions are sophisticated, but still kind. Thelma is wholly at ease in meeting us. She is nothing like I what expected.

The Morrison house is small, clean and quaint. The furniture inside looks rich and simple. The house presents as if it is a small section of a large mansion—yet carries a palpable homey feel.

Leah and I follow Thelma to a small room at the rear of the house. Thelma hesitates in entering, as we can clearly overhear Tom in conversation.

"Simply return to the moment, the only true reality. Review your long bunker shot fundamentals. Fundamentals are *below you* only as a life raft is below you. You were fortunate to have this reminder on such a grand stage. Sleep well tonight and practice well this week to come, with renewed respect and wonder. A much deeper feel may now enter and make residence in your being. Celebrate your struggle. Do not cuss the outcome of the matters of the day. All events are necessary. *Be* and *let be*. Today you have gained an invaluable experience, a great blessing. *Do* and *let do*. Today you evolve by necessity as a player—and as a person."

"Sundays," Thelma whispers with a smile.

Tournament Sunday? I wonder who is calling. Could it be a PGA Tour player? My eyes are as big as cue balls.

Tom chuckles. "Anytime, young friend," he says. "You have earned this most enlightening moment. Congratulations. Move happily along."

Then silence.

Thelma confidently senses that the moment is right to lead us into the room. We enter quietly. Tom is seated, with his ear to the phone. He calmly rises, offering Leah and I a seat through gesture and checks his watch. He continues speaking, commenting that company has arrived and that he must end the call.

Tom hangs up and smiles kindly at Leah and I. "Right on time, folks. You respect my time and your own. That makes me feel very good."

I smile at Leah, who looks surprised.

Tom offers his hand to Leah. "My name is Tom Morrison. Please call me Tom. You must be Leah. Thank you for coming."

"Thank you for the having me, Tom," Leah replies gracefully.

"Would you folks like a drink? Water? Fresh juice? Green tea?" Tom asks.

We both chose water and Tom leaves in pursuit.

Thelma is now seated peacefully in a corner rocking chair, holding a teacup and smiling. Her legs are crossed at the ankles. She rocks lightly. "Walk around the room, kids. It is full of life—and love," she says softly.

Leah and I smile and begin to walk the room. It is active, yet somehow uncluttered, like the rest of the house. Family and miscellaneous pictures adorn the walls. All are housed in matching thin, dark-cherry wood frames. The largest picture is of the Morrison family. Tom and Thelma appear to have three children and eight grandchildren.

"You have a beautiful family," Leah says to Thelma.

"Thank you, Leah. They are the joy of our lives."

Leah smiles, nudges me with her elbow and flashes a "Thelma's nice" look. I nod back, signaling, "I agree".

Two of the men in the family picture look strangely familiar. I drop my shoulders and laugh to myself. They are the men who parked their vans so close to the sidecar during the alignment lesson. Tom had arranged the whole thing—using his sons as bait, nonetheless. A family conspiracy!

I notice several plaques in a trophy case and point them out to Leah. They are from various youth and church groups. A message of thanks to Tom or Thelma or both is engraved on each. What have they done to help, I wonder? Was it the same way that Tom is helping me?

Who are these people? Are they saints? Are they angels? For sure, they're not just *regular people*. Are they?

Framed pictures of famous golfers adorn an entire wall. I recognize Harry Vardon, Bobby Jones, Patty Berg, Gene Sarazen, Babe Zaharias, Byron Nelson, Betsy Rawls, Ben Hogan, Arnold Palmer, Hale Irwin, Jack Nicklaus, Tom Watson, Nancy Lopez, Ernie Els, Retief Goosen, Phil Mickelson and Tiger Woods; and also a whole bunch of Canadian greats—Stan Leonard, Al Balding, Marlene Stewart-Streit, Wilf Homenuik, Moe Norman, George Knudson, Gary Cowan, Ben Kern, Sandra Post-McDermid, Dave Barr, Dan Halldorson, Dawn Coe-Jones, Jim Nelford, Rick Gibson, Richard Zokol, Ray Stewart, Jerry Anderson, Jim Rutledge, Glen Hnatiuk, Lori Kane, Mike Weir. Holy Cow—does he know any of these people? Or does he just collect pictures of golfers?

I remember how crisply he hit those iron shots when he taught me sequence. Is it possible he has played with any of these great players? Or taught them? Gus said Tom was a great player in his day. Was he that good? Ben said Tom *guides* some professionals. Were any of these the players who he means? I am intrigued beyond words. I also suspect that Tom will never answer if I ask.

"Here you are, folks." Tom enters the room, stopping my train of thought. "Two waters. Please sit down. Make yourselves at home."

Leah and I sit together on a cherry-red leather love seat.

"I recognize two of the men in your family picture, Tom," I remark dryly.

Tom smiles. "And they recognize the importance of basic cornerstones—and enjoy helping. Alex and Darryl are both very giving of their time—an excellent character trait."

I have a million questions for Tom.

"You've collected many pictures of golfers I noticed. Are they your favourites?"

"They are all intriguing, for different reasons—as is everyone," he says. "Each have developed their golf skills to a high level, each through very different paths and techniques, and each under very different circumstances."

"How do you know so much about these players, Tom?" I pry.

"That is not important, Billy. What is important is that as different as these great players are and as different as their paths have been, one trait is consistent with them—and all people."

Leah and I stare silently at Tom.

Thelma's voice playfully emerges, as if *taking the baton* from Tom. "They have experienced a natural desire to self-actualize, to reach their highest potential—a function of what some call *conscience*," she says. "Each of these accomplished players has uniquely come to trust the great Inside Voice that whispers softly 'I am and I can' over the many fear-rooted outside voices that insist 'you aren't and you can't.'"

The room becomes still.

Tom smiles at Thelma, as if to *re-accept the baton*. "The sooner one becomes aware of their grace within, the more lightly *and* swiftly one then travels. We are all of one *Spirit*, infinite and continuous. Plants and animals have come to be the true experts. Observe and marvel as the tree bends willingly in the wind, free and easy, content to be *all that it is*."

The room again is silent.

Tom and Thelma sit peacefully.

Leah and I shuffle awkwardly.

"Tell me about yourself, Leah," Tom asks unobtrusively, changing the subject for our sakes. "What are your interests?"

Leah adjusts her position and nervously clears her throat. "Well—actually—I like to—write—and read mostly—in fact, I think I'd like to—be a writer—someday."

I can't believe it. I've never asked Leah this most basic life question. I've never known what she wants to do with her life. Be a writer? I suddenly feel pathetic. Have I been so wrapped up in my own life that I don't know what my own girlfriend likes to do? Or wants to be? Leah and I have been dating for over a year now and Tom asks her this question in the first few minutes of knowing her. Do I want professional golf this badly?

"What do you like to write, dear?" Thelma asks.

"I—I don't really know—I just like to write—I just write letters and poems to my friends and to my family so far—but I enjoy the use of language—for expression."

Leah has written many romantic love letters to me in the past. I often pull them from my closet and read them, over and over and over again. She would make an excellent romance novelist. Heck, with her talent, she'd make an excellent anything. I wish I could be alone with her and tell her so right now.

"I encourage you to begin to write even more, Leah," Tom says. "It may become a love in your life, as golf may be in Billy's."

I manage a polite smile.

"The space available for love in our lives is without end," Tom continues. "It is our most basic nature. Take time to discover who you truly are, then be that person. It is that simple—and that difficult." Tom smiles. "Choose your venture, trade or vocation based both on love *and* contribution to the world. Pursue it with passion. Leonardo Da Vinci wrote: 'Make your work to be in keeping with your purpose.' You will be far ahead to start immediately. Life pursuits may bring many riches; but riches are meaningless, even dangerous, if the heart is not first rich."

Tom and Thelma sit with pleasure in silence.

Leah and I fidget.

Tom points to me with his chin. "Billy is about to discover whether golf is truly a love of his. His passion for the game appears to equal that of anyone I have worked with. Love and sense of contribution unite to form a strong vision that allow us to weather storms and push forward during periods of challenge and struggle. DiVinci wrote: 'Where the spirit does not work with the hand, there is no art.' Explore your writing as soon as possible, Leah."

Leah begins to stir excitedly—and so do I. Finally, some feedback from Tom. He has said so little *about me* up to this point. I had no idea if he even knows I like golf, let alone love it.

" 'Whatever you do or dream you can do, begin it. Boldness has genius and magic and power in it.' Johann Wolfgang von Goethe wrote that," Thelma adds."

Leah laughs wonderment. "I can't imagine that you two have ever struggled—at anything. You both seem so content."

Thelma smiles and answers immediately. "Everyone will struggle at everything, dear. It is a necessary part of life. Expect it. Welcome it. It is a very real friend, necessitating change and growth. Challenge makes us identify and overcome fear, allowing us to evolve by testing our faith in seemingly the most difficult of times. The English poet, William Wordsworth, wrote: 'Wisdom is oftentimes nearer when we stoop than when we soar.' Tom and I are content because of struggle, not despite it. We continue to accept and appreciate its lessons every day."

An oven buzzer suddenly rings in the distance, claiming our attention—and as if to end class.

"Dinner will be ready shortly," Thelma announces, without missing a beat. "Shall we move to the dining room?"

*

Dinner is remarkable—and very healthy. Thelma serves salmon, asparagus, peppers and spinach salad. We drink water, flavored and nourished by fresh lemon slices.

The conversation at the dinner table is much more care free than in the sitting room. Stories are exchanged mostly of memorable events within each of our families. Leah shares many stories that I have never heard. Some are about her, her Mom and her sister and the fun they enjoyed before Mr. Bremont entered their lives. Some occur after Mr. Bremont joined their family. I learn how much happiness Leah has in her family. I am able to gain even more respect for her mom and Mr. Bremont. I understand why Leah and Robin are so well adapted within their apparently *broken home*.

It is fascinating hearing about Leah's life. There is certainly more than one recipe for happiness within a family. My life perspective is being stretched. We laugh out loud many times. Leah and I hold hands under the table.

Tom and Thelma share a more traditional relationship and family, similar to that of my own Mom and Dad. The degree of effect my family has had on me never quite seemed to register, until lately. My awareness of the important role of family has become more conscious during these last few weeks. I guess I've always taken it for granted. What an important job it is to be a parent.

"Will you kids have some green tea while I clear the dishes?" Thelma asks.

"I'll help, Thelma," Leah says.

Leah must sense my desire for more one-on-one time with Tom before our lessons end. Either that or *Leah* wants more one-on-one time with *Thelma*.

"Thank you, girls," Tom says kindly. "I will make the tea."

Thelma smiles at Tom.

*

I realize that this will be the last meeting for Tom and I as strictly *guide* and *pupil*. I feel sad on one hand, knowing I'll soon miss his company and his wisdom. On the other hand, I'm excited to soak up one more night of insight. I still have many questions.

Tom prepares green tea for everyone, then leads me back to the sitting room where we settle.

"Leah is a wonderful girl," he says matter-of-factly.

"Yeah, she's the best," I agree.

"You will play a very important role in her life, Billy." Tom's voice now takes on guide tone, "and she will in yours."

"I like her a lot—more each day, it seems," I confess. "But we're so young. I get focused on golf sometimes and I neglect her—I don't mean to."

"Love her unconditionally, Billy," Tom offers immediately. "That is your only responsibility to her—and to yourself. It is the greatest gift one can give. Unconditional love is the essence of life. Your paths are early. The type of love to develop will become evident in proper time."

"Love her unconditionally?" I rebut. "That sounds pretty corny, Tom. You think I should just say '*yes*' to everything she asks and agree with everything she does and says? I mean, I think I love her and all that, but I have ideas, too."

"Do your Mother and Father say 'yes' to everything you ask?" Tom counters. "Do they agree with everything you do and say?"

"No, but they're my parents," I return.

"Unconditional love means being *caring, patient* and *respectful*, but most of all *honest*—whether to yourself, to a son or daughter or to another. No recipe for unconditional love includes the ingredient of *naiveté*."

"Yeah, I guess—" I stammer, "but I still don't know if I can be *loving*, as you say, all of the time."

"It is a learning process, Billy, just like the golf swing. Gain knowledge, apply it and review it regularly—no different. It is simple, but demands effort."

There he goes again with that *simple* stuff.

"Have you and Thelma been together since you were both young?" I ask.

"Since we were seventeen," Tom answers rhythmically. "She has always been her own person and I have always been mine. Our paths brought us together to be family. This has always been clear to us both, yet I would have been there for her no matter what path presented—she is that special to me."

"Did you have other girlfriends before Thelma?" I pry.

"Other girlfriends, yes," Tom says. "Other Thelmas, no."

"When did you know she was the one for you?" I ask.

"Within two weeks," Tom returns calmly.

"I thought you said I shouldn't rush things with Leah?"

"I said you should love her unconditionally. *Your* proper role will establish in *your* proper time."

I'll miss Tom's efficient reasoning.

"Billy, ask me any important question relating to our weeks together and I will answer," he says. "Now is the time."

I hesitate. Any question? Yeah. Now *is* the time!

I swallow and take a deep breath. "Well—I've always wondered—what level of golf did you play? Were you ever on the PGA Tour?"

Tom responds immediately. "You are very early in your journey, Billy. Trinkets and titles easily seduce you. It is not an important question. Learn first your cornerstones. As the great Lao-tsu wrote: 'He who knows others is wise; he who knows himself is enlightened.'" Tom's tone is kind, not judgmental. "This is understandable. You are only beginning to discover that what is most important is inside, like joy and gratitude, and not outside, like adulation. Trinkets and titles come and go, acting as temporary food for the ego." Tom sounds flippant yet celebratory. "Look deep inside instead to sense the presence of *Spirit*. Notice how ego sees Spirit as a 'lesser-than'. Dismiss this chimera of ego, Billy, and rejoice at what is true. Your life is *already* a miracle! You are 70 trillion conscious cells working together, in harmony—against all odds. You possess all you could ever wish for. Don't let the impostor *ego* tell you otherwise—don't sell yourself short. Most take life so much for granted that it may *seem* not to be a miracle." He pauses. "Ask Ben about ego and adulation when you begin to work with him."

Adulation? When I work with Ben? What kind of comment is that? Is Tom teasing me? He must not know that Ben turned me down flat as a student.

"I don't know if Ben will *ever* work with me," I mutter.

"He will, Billy," Tom says coolly and sips his tea. "Ben and I have met. He has asked me to have you contact him as soon as possible."

What? Did I hear right? Am I dreaming? Is it finally happening? My boyhood idol has agreed to help me with my game?

"Ben said that?" I chirp. "Are you sure?"

"Of course I'm sure."

"Thank you, Tom. Thanks for asking him."

"I didn't ask him," Tom says, vacant of emotion. "You did, two weeks ago. You alone have earned this opportunity through respect and honest commitment and will continue to advance through more of the same. Ben sees this in you, as I do."

I sense an encouraging tone from Tom, one that says, "Go for it, kid, you have what it takes!" I feel more passionate now than ever.

"I want to play golf for a living more than anything in the world, Tom," I blurt. "I'll do whatever it takes to get there!" The comment just spilled out.

"Whoa, Billy. Slow down," Tom's calming voice advises. "You have a passion for the game. Accept that that is enough for now—and for always. Pursue your passion for golf without fear. It can take you on a wonderful, life-long journey. Where to, will show in time, but doesn't really matter."

"That sounds like what you told me about Leah."

"The same," Tom says. "You don't own golf and you don't own Leah. You will never control either directly. Ego has the need to control, but now you know—*ego is not real*. Love golf unconditionally, just as Leah—just as all of your life interests. You will never be disillusioned or dissatisfied. You will fulfill your highest role, at all times."

Tom's answer, though sensible, still frustrates me. I need to know what he *really* thinks about my *ambitions*.

"Don't you think I can make it onto the PGA tour?"

"It is indeed one possible outcome—one of many." Tom remains serenely still, producing a calculated silence.

One of many? How dare him. He's never even seen me play. He doesn't *really* know me. I have the best junior record of any player *ever* from The Hat! He doesn't know what's in my heart! In my guts!

"A lot of people doubt me, Tom, but I didn't think you were one of them," I say, feeling defensive and shocked by his answers.

"I have as much confidence in your potential as in anyone's," he offers, maintaining unflinching eye contact. Then Tom leans toward me from the hip joints and speaks sternly.

"You are asking the age-old question, Billy: 'Do I get exactly what I want from life?' The answer is: 'probably not.' Thankfully, life rarely gives us *exactly what we think we want*. Instead, it presents to us *what is*. Only a minute percentage that dream to play on the PGA Tour will do so. If every talented golfer to dream this dream were to make it, there would be no PGA Tour. What then?

"I don't think I'm just *every talented golfer* as you say, Tom," my rebuttal continues. "I've had a pretty darn good record—that I'm proud of. I've had attention from US schools—a lot of them. Doesn't that mean anything?"

Tom hears, but doesn't accept, my request for "special status".

"Your plea parallels the story of the waitress serving soup in the diner. A patron asks, 'What is this?' to which she replies, 'Why, it is *bean soup.*' The patron says 'I don't care what it's *been*, what is it *now*?'" Tom's tone is anything but playful. "Do not handicap your potential, Billy—or your dream. You will get many chances to prove that you are this person you dream to be. Be sure to be prepared. Pave your path with knowledge, application and review, rather than with jabber and posturing. You will always be in your proper place—and that place *will always be remarkable*." Tom produces a reflective pause. "Application includes continually creating a clear vision of your short- and long-term goals. Many factors may challenge you and change you along your journey. Adjust your goals accordingly, if necessary. Pursue your passions free of the fear of both failure and success, free of both past and future. Be present in your life. Learn from the great teacher called *struggle*. Benjamin Franklin wrote: 'The things which hurt, instruct.' Review your fundamentals regularly. Honor that which is simple. Be grateful *today* for the gifts in your life. Family, friends, health, ability, and opportunity are immense blessings. Be thankful now."

"Dreams are absolutely necessary, Billy. Neither fear them nor be flippant about their role. Einstein said: 'Imagination is

everything. It is a preview of life's coming attractions.'
Napoleon Hill wrote: "Whatever your mind can conceive and
believe, it can achieve.' But be aware, Billy, life-dreams are
only achieved through the great dream-maker, *presence*. Enjoy
fully the experience of *today*, of *now,* of what is *real*. Healthy
thoughts and actions *today* are your only connection to the
illusion of *tomorrow*."

Tom rises and quietly glides over to his small desk, slides
open the lap drawer and removes two 3″x 5″ recipe cards. He
offers them to me. "Please accept these special cards as
keepsakes. In combination, they are most diverse and powerful
directors."

I accept them and read. Each contains a neatly hand-written
message:

Card #1

"When you are inspired by some great purpose, some
extraordinary project, all your thoughts break their bounds:
Your mind transcends limitations, your consciousness
expands in every direction and you find yourself in a new,
great and wonderful world. Dormant forces, faculties and
talents become alive, and you discover yourself to be a
greater person by far than you ever dreamed yourself to be."

—Patanjali

Card #2

"Such gardens are not made by Singing: '…Oh, how
beautiful' and Sitting in the shade."

—Rudyard Kipling

Of course! Nothing Tom offers suggests that I give up my dream. Tom is focusing me on a healthy approach to *now*. Be happy *now*, not *when*. He forecasts nothing. Why would he? There are no guarantees. Worrying about tomorrow distracts me from *today*, from *this moment*. My future depends on my thoughts and actions *now*. I feel Tom's wisdom crawling inside me, settling my mind, easing my fears and uncertainties.

"Thanks," I sigh as I pack the cards neatly into my note pad.

I feel myself growing and changing by the second, but I still have important questions for Tom. I still itch for guidance and clarification.

"Tom, you've never asked to see my golf swing. Why not?"

He nods in tactful agreement. "I am a specialist, Billy, a guide. I guide people towards an efficient and joyous approach to golf—and to life—reminding people of *simple* by guiding their senses towards the everyday presence of natural lessons and laws. *Obvious* is not *obvious* to most. To others, *obvious is not enough.*" Tom sorrowfully shakes his head, as if catching a best friend in a lie. "Society commonly sets unrealistic conditions for true success and happiness. Without simplicity, the faces of confusion, disarray and inadequacy prevail. They are meaninglessly rampant in all pursuits. The strength of simple cornerstones can organize and rid folks of these burdens. In golf, **grip, alignment, balance and sequence**—on every putt, chip, pitch, bunker shot, half swing, three-quarter swing, full swing and trouble shot. In health, **food, oxygen, water and a healthy nervous system**—supplied maximally as daily habits. In relationships, whether with yourself or others, practise consistent **caring, honesty, patience and respect**. Most all difficulties stem from a misunderstanding or a misapplication of a fundamental cornerstone or cornerstones—in any pursuit."

"Simple, simple, simple, Billy. Nature's lessons are constantly around to remind us of this truth. Continue to *look deeply* and to *think for yourself.* There is no need to watch you hit a golf ball to guide you to these principles. Ben Farr is a CPGA professional. He teaches golf and is trained properly to do so. Make use of your golf professional—invest in yourself. Your golf skills will advance much further than by chasing around the newest club or gadget."

I stir with excitement at this overwhelming learning experience *and* at the reminder of my newly formed passage to Ben.

"Fundamentals solid first, "FSF,' Billy. True wisdom will be close at hand in any pursuit, be it golf, health, business, sales, relationships, education, art, sports or you name it. In all you do, practise the skill of *presence*, the great dream-maker. Happiness, health and skill are available to us all—right now. Sense the great *Inside Voice* within you and the road to fearless living begins."

*

I stew nervously over my final two questions. Each is a direct challenge to my new found friend and mentor.

"Are you—against medicine, Tom—drugs and surgery, I mean?"

Tom smiles. "What's red and smells like blue paint, Billy?" he asks.

I gaze at Tom like a lost puppy. "I don't know—"

"Red paint!" he snaps playfully. "Are fundamental answers *too fundamental*? Modern health is no exception in this oversight. Do you remember the concept of OCF from our alignment lesson?"

"I sure do, Original Causative Factor!" I return confidently, feeling like the teacher's pet.

"Society regularly accepts the latest and greatest symptomatic quick-fix as their complete health solution, without any consideration as to OCF's. Nature, on the other hand, offers powerful daily health solutions that address OCF's directly—true health cornerstones that are no different in principle today than one hundred years ago." Tom's rhythm slows subtly. "If one desires optimum health, one must ask the question: 'Have I truly mastered my own daily health cornerstones?' Our true health state is our own responsibility. To be genuinely healthy requires regular learning, practice and review."

"The same as cornerstones in golf," I say in a moment of clarity

"The same as cornerstones in any pursuit—FSF. The success of a quick-fix in golf without solid fundamentals will indeed also be short-lived." Tom shifts slightly in his seat. "I am not *against* medicine, Billy. Medical emergencies can require symptomatic comforting or invasive attention or both. Diagnostic testing and research can provide invaluable information and scientific insight. We are lucky to have this security. Rather, I am *for* healthy daily habits, *for* personal responsibility and *for* addressing the cause of dis-ease. I am a proponent that authentic health occurs only when we respect and care for the needs of the wisest doctor of all—the one inside us all."

The *wisest doctor of all*! I like that! And I *have* felt more vibrant and I *have* had much more energy since learning and improving my personal health cornerstones. Maybe it's true that unlimited health potential is already inside us after all.

I sip my tea in silence and smile sheepishly. I have one question left, the hardest of all for me to ask—yet I feel compelled. Tom Morrison is so wise—and has helped me so much. It bothers me that people look down on him, including Gus. Here goes nothing.

"Why do you pick range balls, Tom?" I blurt abruptly. "You have so much to say and so many people to guide. Why don't you just quit?"

I angle my body in anguish, anticipating Tom's disapproval.

Instead, to my surprise, he becomes jubilant. "Hallelujah! And congratulations, Billy!" Tom snarls. "You have asked the only question that remains for your learning enjoyment!"

Relief floods my body. Tom isn't insulted at all. Instead, he is genuinely elated. He takes a moment to settle and then replies in a manner I've come to respect—with both ease and strength.

"Picking range balls very much reflects the basis of my life work, Billy," he replies proudly. "My first job as a young boy was on a driving range. As I grew up, I developed my golf swing through much effort on various driving ranges. Driving ranges have taught me about simple truth, patience and respect—for the game, for myself and for life. They have taught me about persistence and have given me the confidence to observe and explore life's challenges, through learning, application, and review—rather simple really."

Tom breaks for a sip of tea.

"My role on the driving range is no different than my guiding role with you has been. With each, I present simple vehicles housing an immense opportunity for learning and enlightenment. The hand exercise device, the greenhouse, the sidecar motorcycle, the circus and the football game films— they are no different than each range ball I return. Each offers a vast amount of wisdom and pure truth for the next user to discover. Only ego sees my role on the driving range as important or unimportant."

Another peaceful pause from Tom and another sip of tea.

"The driving range is the conscience of the game, Billy. When I observe golfers practicing alone on the driving range, they are free of façade, facing the pure reality that the game has to offer. They are in wondrous awe, as they should be. On the golf course, most act as if the game is *small* and they are *big*— their attention shifts to ego protection. Eventually the game calls their bluff and presents a moment framed by challenge, conscious attention and unfamiliarity, and next, *insult*—the ultimate resting place of all ego. Then, it's back to the driving range! A wonderful parody, don't you think?"

I chuckle in marvel of Tom's perspective and perception.

"The opportunity to gain universal truth on the driving range is immense, Billy. If a day were to arrive when no driving range ball needs to be picked, it would be a sad day indeed. That day, humans would be wiser than nature, golfers would be wiser than golf, and challenge and struggle would no longer be teachers and sages. That day, the words scribed by the philosophers of all ages would become hogwash." He pauses and smiles deviously. "I am aware of no driving range to become obsolete as such."

"Me neither!" I gurgle aggressively, in awe of nature and the game and the man before me.

"There are two more reasons why I pick range balls throughout the summer months, Billy," Tom continues casually. "I will tell you reason two and *you* will tell me reason three."

"But I don't know reason three, Tom," I concede helplessly.

"But you do, Billy," Tom says. "Let me start with reason two. Reason three is well within your reach."

Tom adjusts his posture subtly, as I try to imagine what *he imagines* I know.

"Reason two: 'Work banishes those three great evils: boredom, vice and poverty.' The French philosopher Voltaire wrote this insight over two centuries ago. I have always observed his words to be true. When one discovers a trade or vocation or project to pursue with passion, one is indeed blessed—as Voltaire suggests. I enjoy the participation, contribution and insight that my work returns. My time during the summer months is well served on the driving range, rest assured. Consider it *'Continuing Education' for the guide profession.*" He smiles. "Pursuing the study of the game of golf may be *your* version of Voltaire's salvation."

I nod, deeply intrigued by Tom's comment. How much more can my mind be expanded in such a short time? Endlessly, it seems—when allowed to! Until now, I've never allowed myself to accept concepts like "love," "spirit," "nature" and "gratitude" for fear of being ridiculed by my friends. There's that word again, "fear". I haven't missed it at all these last few weeks.

It's now up to me to supply Tom's third answer. Through his body language, he's allowing me some extra time to think. What is within my reach? *Through the summer months*—what does he mean by that? What's the difference between summer and winter?

"You can be outside!" I snarl reflexively. That's it! "You can breathe fresh air! You can get exercise! The third cornerstone of health—of course—*oxygen*!"

Tom growls an explosive "Good boy!" that lifts him from his chair.

I figured it out! I did know it—and wait—there's more. "You enjoy being on the driving range too, Tom! And you enjoy the sense of accomplishment and contribution. That's good for your *nervous system*, the fourth health cornerstone. Your work is healthy!"

"Right you are, Billy! Right you are, kid! Congratulations! Correct on both counts!" he cheers.

Tom and I celebrate raucously. Leah and Thelma must be wondering what in the world is happening.

"You have graduated, Billy! You are your own thinker!" Tom says joyously, "and you always will be! You have learned learning!" He nods proudly. "You are now ready to travel the road of fearless action, a road that will present many more wonders and challenges."

My celebration stalls as I suddenly come to a poignant realization. "A road that would have chewed me up and spit me out if it weren't for you, Tom." I pause deeply. "How can I ever repay you?"

"You can give me your watch, for starters," Tom prods, still energized. "It is darned accurate."

I let out a well-timed, emotion-releasing bellow.

As my laughter settles, Tom leans to me with a timeless stare, squares his torso to mine and clutches my right shoulder decisively with his rising left hand. "Your path will be up to you and you alone, Billy, though others will help," Tom's voice takes on a tone of sullen conviction. "Pursue your life with caring, honesty, patience and respect, free of fear, as will I. Continue to learn and grow, as will I. Continue to bring love into your life, as will I. We all are of one Spirit, despite the efforts of ego to divide us. What you do to others along your path, you also do to yourself. Continue to be present, where Spirit alone shines. Remember that something as simple as a golf club brought us together—simplicity has far reaching affects." His stare becomes even more intense. "Give back as you have received, Billy. *You alone* determine your impact on and your contribution to the world. You have an immense opportunity to inspire others through example. Great feats occur when our focus is on needs greater than our own."

I feel both drained and strong. I nod admiringly and set down my teacup. Unbeknownst to me, tears have welled up in the corner of my eyes. My throat is heavy. My heart pounds eerily. I am deeply humbled by tonight's messages—and by the knowledge and spirit of the man in front of me. I know he is asking me to pass on his wisdom and his generosity—to pass on *his love*. I feel immensely empowered.

In silence, we stand, shake hands firmly and begin to make our way back to the kitchen.

The walk back is dreamlike. My body is light and alive. I am fully aware of my breathing and my heartbeat—and of the vibrant nerve energy inexplicably coordinating my body. The walk marks an end to a most memorable chapter in my life. I know my one-on-one time with range picker Old Tom Morrison is over. The experience—I also know—will last a lifetime.

Chapter 12

Change

It's the Tuesday before the Victoria Day Golf Tournament. I'm stretching beside the driving range tee at the Connaught Golf Course before my afternoon lesson with Ben Farr. My water bottle and banana lie beside my golf bag. I stop my warm-up momentarily for a sip and a few bites.

My formal golf lessons with Ben Farr started about a month ago, soon after finishing with Tom. Ben and I met Tuesdays and Fridays for the first two weeks and Tuesdays only for the last two. He's been fantastic to work with, honest and demanding.

I'll always remember the start of my lessons with Ben. First, he commended me for being on time. Next, he proudly displayed a fairway wood, glued his eyes to mine sternly and announced, "This is a golf club, Billy." He went on to review the fundamental parts of the club, periodically testing me with questions, some very basic. I answered each with zest. He spoke to me about shaft lengths and flex theories, club lofts and lies, club design and more. He spoke to me about some of the legends of the game—Willie Park, Tom Morris, Allan Robertson, Harry Vardon, Walter Hagen, Gene Sarazen, Mickey Wright, Bobby Jones, Babe Zaharias, Byron Nelson, Ben Hogan, Sam Snead, Arnold Palmer, Gary Player, Jack Nicklaus, Nancy Lopez, Tiger Woods and Annika Soremstam.

He encouraged me to become familiar with the game's fascinating history, as well as with the rich history of Canadian golf.

"Study the golf history of your own country, Billy. The world golf community agrees, Canada has produced three of the best ball strikers of their time," Ben said proudly, "Norman, Knudson and Weir. There are also arguments for others to be placed in the same breath. As well, Canadian Bob Panasik is the youngest player to make the cut in a PGA Tour event, at the age of fifteen. Sandra Post-McDermid is the youngest winner of a modern major, winning the LPGA Championship at the age of twenty. The Royal Montreal Golf Club is the oldest golf club in North America and the Canadian Open is the third oldest professional championship in the world. The Canadian Professional Golf Tour is saturated with world-class players and has produced dozens and dozens of PGA Tour stars. Our country is rich in golf history and tradition. You'll be much richer from the study."

His approach was humbling and familiar. I sensed Ben's love for the game as I had Tom Morrison's.

The majority of the rest of our lesson time has been spent checking and refining my cornerstones—grip, alignment, balance and sequence—using videotape. Ben is objective, if nothing else. He doesn't sugar coat yet isn't harsh. To my surprise, all of my cornerstones have needed work—a lot of work! I had won so many junior tournaments with poor fundamentals. Ben assured me it would be difficult to reach a new level without change. He's also given me a series of basic putting, chipping, pitching and bunker drills for my practice sessions.

When we first started together, I expressed concerns as to how changes to my swing would affect my short-term performance.

"There are no guarantees in golf or in life," Ben said. "If I tell you that change will help immediately and it doesn't, I become a liar. If I say you will struggle yet you improve immediately, I am also a liar. I will only say the truth, Billy—change is necessary."

Ben compared changing one's golf swing to changing a poor habit in one's health or in one's life: awkward for the short-term—necessary and satisfying for the long term.

"People resist change out of fear; fear of being out of their comfort zone, of ridicule from peer groups or of failure or success at the new challenge. Resist necessary change and resist growth." Ben chuckled. "I've been on both sides of the coin, Billy. I suggest you discard fear and welcome necessary change."

It's funny. I crave water now and not soda. If two months ago someone told me this was possible, I would have told them they were nuts. Change *is* possible.

In checking my cornerstones, Ben noticed I was holding the club too much in the palm of my left hand. He felt this was interrupting the natural waist-high hinging of my wrists during my backswing. Instead, he said my hands were becoming too active and my left arm was collapsing.

"The left arm must remain extended during the backswing, Billy—relaxed, but extended. When the left arm collapses, check the *original causative factors* of improper grip pressure, poor grip position, weak postural balance or a faulty backswing sequence. I'm sure Tom showed you the value of passing the grip handle lightly between the left hand and right hand. He also would have shown you the value of supporting the club in your left hand grip fingers—the middle, ring and pinky. Review this information. The resultant grip position choice will allow a natural hinging of your left wrist. Your left arm can then extend naturally."

He was right and showed me so on film.

Ben set up to a fairway wood in his address position, a position I remember well from watching him years ago. Man, he looked solid!

He spoke as he mimicked the backswing. "Turn your upper body fully against the resistance of your lower body while maintaining balanced posture. The lower body is your foundation and must remain stable. The left arm extends and the left wrist hinges naturally at waist-high, such that the club shaft becomes parallel with the target line and power line at the top of the backswing."

He held the position at the top of his backswing. I was inspired. The shaft was indeed parallel with his target and power lines at the top of his backswing.

This grip change gave me more distance immediately by widening my swing arc, the *roundness* or *width* of my swing. I could now get the club easily near parallel (to the ground) at the top of my backswing, without collapsing my left arm. I did feel some awkwardness toward my new grip position at first, but I rapidly adapted. I consciously check it in my pre-shot routine before each shot now.

Next, Ben focused his microscope on my alignment. As Tom had suggested, I was guilty of aligning my body to the *target line* instead of to the *power line*. I was reminded of Tom's example of the two alignment lines of the motorcycle and sidecar. He would have crashed me into the traffic to our right had he not focused the motorcycle on the power line. *I was crashing my own golf alignment!*

"You're aimed at least five yards to the right of your target, Billy," Ben said calmly from behind my target line. "Tom made you aware of the two alignment lines, did he not?"

"Yep," I replied. "The target line and the power line."

"You are aware of them, but are not applying them. Knowledge, application and review—for all cornerstones, Billy. True wisdom requires all three. Very simple. We must clean this up now."

To make up for this poor habit, I'd been *closing*, or *hooding*, the clubface to keep the ball from flying right of my target, the same as Tom told me about *other* golfers. I didn't think I was one of *them*, but there it was, again on video.

The alignment change was difficult, as I had to retrain my *mind's eye*. At first, I felt as if I was aimed a mile to the left of my target upon Ben's correction. He had me blurt out loud "TARGET LINE!" as I aligned my clubface, and "POWER LINE!" as I aligned my body during each set up. I felt like a fool, but I did it. Ben explained to me that involving more senses speeds the progress of any change to your golf swing and your body.

Ben also adjusted my posture, feeling I was too slouched—I was beginning to get an inferiority complex! He showed me on video how I was neglecting to support my lower back properly and also how my chin was tucked down and in. I began to stand taller and bend only *from my hip joints*, as opposed to *from my waist*, another caution of Tom's. I wouldn't have believed my poor posture had I not seen it for myself.

"The flexible disks in your lower back are supported best when there is a subtle forward hollow in the low back," Ben said. "Only then can the trunk rotate maximally and can your balance be maintained. Slouching ruins balance and rotation more than any other single culprit."

Ben had me sit on a bench with hunched posture for demonstration, cross my arms across my chest and turn my trunk as far as possible back and through. He recorded my end points and next had me repeat the experiment with proper posture. Voilà! I turned nearly twice as far. Point taken.

"Balance is poor, at best, when posture is hunched, Billy. Make your body accept true stable neutral through exercise and through conscious repetition of true neutral, as posture. 'Posture lazy' golfers tend to collapse at the first sign of pressure or fatigue. Be able to sense your posture through sensing a stable butt position and a level chin at any point in your swing." He transformed his golf club to imitate a hockey stick while maintaining his proper spinal curves. "You'll never see Medicine Hat Tigers hockey players skating with poor posture.

A *stable butt position and level chin* keeps them from being knocked *onto* their butts."

This change was also awkward at first. My body felt restricted. Ben provided an interesting quote from Matthias Alexander, the Tasmanian-born actor turned therapist: 'When you're wrong, what's right feels wrong.' Now, through repetition, my balance feels solid and my shoulder turn has improved dramatically.

Ben showed me a series of simple stretches to aid these posture changes. The stretches are mostly done standing up, so I can do them anywhere. They have become relatively easy through repetition and familiarity and have given my body an improved sense of well-being.

Tom taught me how important and overlooked the spinal posture is to one's health. Now, I'm living it. I'm even sitting better in school *and* at the dinner table! I'm feeling much more energetic.

Ben next observed faults in my sequence. For one, I was too quick in the transition between my backswing and downswing. My momentum moved so quickly back that I was forced to activate my hips too quickly to begin the downswing. This quick backswing motion back played havoc with my center of gravity, moving it to the outside of my right foot rather than to the inside at the top of my backswing. The result was a lot of "pull hook" shots, definitely my weakness, especially under pressure. Ben had me lighten my grip pressure, making it impossible for me to whip the club back quickly.

"Snead said: 'Hold the club like you are holding a small bird. Not too tight that you hurt it, not too loose that it gets away.'" Ben said. "And he did just fine."

It sounded like Tom's "give up control to gain control" Knudson bit. This was the toughest change of all. I felt like I didn't have control of the club initially. But, man, when I hit a shot well with lighter grip pressure, it soared like a rocket—and sounded like Tom's shots during our sequence lesson.

The changes seem like a lot but, as Ben pointed out, nearly all are accomplished during my set up, before any movement begins. I can practice these changes anywhere—at home, at school, in the locker room—anywhere. Ben stressed to me to simply be consistent, allowing my body and mind time to accept the new positions through repetition. He stressed to me to use as many senses as possible when making a change. His suggestions to gain feedback from a mirror for *sight* and to close my eyes for *kinesthetic* feedback helped me immensely.

"Practice these positions regularly, as conscious habit, until they become unconscious habit. Repetition and experience transforms knowledge into wisdom," Ben said. "Your body alone decides how long this will take."

His counsel sounded familiar.

"Good afternoon, Billy. It's a beautiful day," Ben snaps me out of dreamland. "Right on time. You respect our time together, an excellent character trait. I know someone else who would agree."

Ben startles me nearly every lesson day, as Tom used to. And most days, the same rewarding comment about timeliness. And I'm always on time.

"Hi, Ben," I return.

"Are you warmed-up?" he asks, setting up his video camera and tripod behind my target line. This view gives Ben the best look at alignment and balance. Later, he'll view me face on, from a point perpendicular to my shoulders, to check grip and sequence.

"Yeah, all ready to go, Ben," I say, checking my grip on my 7-iron.

"Grip, alignment, balance and sequence." Ben lays two golf clubs down, one to reference the target line, the other to reference the power line. "Let's have a look."

The lesson goes well. I am closer on all counts and Ben is impressed. Ben's watchful eyes steer me immediately, filtering out bad actions before they have a chance to become bad habits. He's been invaluable to me.

"Your swing mechanics have improved dramatically over the last few weeks, Billy," Ben says tranquilly. "How does that make you feel?"

"It feels great, Ben," I say excitedly. "I'm learning proper application."

I'm sure today that Ben will brief me on my mental preparation for the Victoria Day Tournament that starts Saturday—and I'm all ears. What advice will he give me? He's a former touring pro and could probably whip anybody around here. He'll let me in on some great insights, I bet. My mind churns in anticipation.

"Remember a few things, Billy," Ben says sincerely.

Here we go—

"Many people can be positively affected by this great game." Ben hesitates noticeably. "Your talent and enthusiasm may enable you to make a considerable difference in many people's lives. You have natural talent, a supportive family and an excellent work ethic. You have already attracted the attention of both Tom and myself."

He coolly sips his water.

"Remember that the game is not yours, Billy. Accept this truth right now. Pursue it with all the vim and vigour you can muster. It is as honest, pure and rewarding as you envision. Golf will teach you countless truths and natural laws—about people, nature and about yourself. It will never disappoint you—if you respect it."

Another casual swig of water for Ben.

"You will meet others with similar talent and drive, Billy. Respect them. They are lifetime friends, colleagues and teachers, never enemies. Observe the intangibles of skilled players. Try to beat the stuffing out of them when you play, but respect them just the same. They will challenge you to grow and you will challenge them. Some will be availed less opportunity than you, some more. Do not compare. Do not judge. Do not be distracted from your purpose. Count your blessings regularly and respect what is simple. Trust your Inside Voice for focus. Strive to remain free of ego. Continue to accept opportunities for growth as a person, as a player and as a student of the game. There is much to experience, to learn and to develop in order to truly excel as a player—and as a role model."

Ben abruptly put his hand on my shoulder and addresses me with frightening integrity.

"I will say this to you only once, Billy, and never again, so please listen."

Great, some advice about tournament golf, I bet!

"When you are able to give back, do so," Ben pauses. "In a small way, you can make the world a better place. We can all make a big difference in a small way. Golf is for everyone, bringing folks to nature, to themselves and to others. There is no greater gift than giving. Grow and excel and then give back. Make a difference. Leave a legacy for many to follow."

He shakes my hand firmly, turns and begins to walk away.

"Oh—and Billy," he smiles. "Good luck this weekend. Enjoy the tournament. I'll see you back here on Tuesday."

Ben Farr said some nice things about me—some real nice things! I sense my perspective of the game changing rapidly, maybe too rapidly. I play golf mostly with kids my age. They'll think I'm bananas if I share this new attitude with them—I can't talk about this—*or can I?* And that wasn't much of a pep talk for the tournament—*or was it?*

I take a swig of my water, finish my banana and continue hitting practice shots.

Grip, alignment, balance and sequence—grip, alignment, balance, sequence—

Chapter 13

The First Tee

Saturday has arrived, the first day of the Victoria Day Golf Tournament. Dad's caddying for me, as is indicated by the white golf towel draped around his neck. He's crouched like a baseball catcher, returning my practice putts on the practice green.

A quick peek at my watch shows 10:00 am, twenty minutes away from my tee time. Nerves are getting the best of me today. I can sense my legs shaking and my hands sweating. I couldn't eat this morning.

The local media has made a big deal out of the tournament committee's decision to allow me into the tournament. Is it positive or negative for the tournament? Is it good or bad for me? Theories vary as to how I will play. Some pick me to win. Some pick me to fall flat on my face. I don't have a clue who's right.

I recognize most of the local sports writers and TV reporters. They're all here. A camera crew from CHAT TV, the local TV station, filmed me stretching and hitting practice balls earlier this morning. Now they're filming me as I hit practice putts. Will they give me any time to myself before I play? What are they looking for?

"Focus on your routine, Billy, not on them," Dad urges, noticing me noticing them. "They have a job to do, as do you." He reaches into his pocket. "Ben wanted me to give you this."

He hands me a small, neatly folded piece of paper. I unwrap it and read:

"Life is a daring adventure or nothing."

—Helen Keller

Holy cow! What a gesture by Ben—and such a powerful and appropriate message. It sparks a surge of strength and perspective from deep inside me. A daring adventure. It *is* a daring adventure and I *want* to play against these guys! I *want* the opportunity! I *want* to test myself under these conditions!

I immediately feel more settled. I feel as if Ben is with me. Is Ben here? I haven't seen him. I search, but instead noticed the size of the swelling crowd massing around the first tee. Again, my mind wonders nervously.

I notice that the Kerry Slinger and Gary Oliwal group is about to tee off. They're one group ahead of me and are among the many great local golfers playing, especially Slinger. He's always the guy to beat around here. He's won this tournament ten times if he's won it once. He knows every inch of this golf course. Once an Alberta Amateur Champion and twice an Alberta Mid-Amateur Champion, he can play. He's represented Alberta in the Willington Cup matches against other Canadian provinces twice.

Oliwal's more of a bomber. If he keeps the golf ball in play, he'll be a threat. Oliwal's a lot younger than Slinger—mid-thirties, I think—but needs to control the ball better before he'll break through provincially or nationally. Oliwal's never won the Victoria Day Tournament, but he's been in contention lots.

Filling out their foursome is Al Shmaltz, another former Alberta Amateur Champion and multiple Victoria Day winner, and Gil Nasland, both from Calgary.

I'm paired today with John Nasland, Gil's older brother—oh—and did I mention?—a flippin' Canadian golf legend! What a day to meet him—along with all of these other distractions!

I asked for this. Am I biting off more than I can chew? A tidal wave of fear again floods my mind and body. It couldn't have arrived at a worse time. I feel sick. My hands begin sweating worse than before. Will I even be able to hold onto the golf club? Will I make a fool of myself in front of all of these people? Am I really ready for this?

"Slow your pace down, Billy. You're going a mile a minute," Dad half-whispers, reaching into his pocket again. "Tom wanted me to give you this."

He hands me another small, neatly folded piece of paper. I unwrap it nervously and read:

"We must dare, and dare again, and go on daring."

—Georges Danton

What a thoughtful gesture—by Tom this time! I sigh and once again shake myself out of fear mode. I feel courageous and thankful and silly all at the same time—silly for granting so much power again to my fears.

"Thanks, Dad," I say, consciously slowing down my actions.

"Don't thank me," he smiles. "Thank your coaches."

"Thanks for being here, I mean. It helps." I smile. "You're my coach too, you know."

Dad nods.

The others in my group are Fred VanDerkadden, a former Alberta Amateur and Canadian Mid-Amateur Champion from St. Albert, and Jim Alfman, a bomber and former Victoria Day and Alberta Mid-Amateur champion from Red Deer.

In the group behind me is another popular Hat golfer and defending champion, Donny Valen. He was the last local junior before me to make a big splash nationally. Donny's older brother, Ricky, was the best local junior before that. Ricky's another group back.

They're all wandering the practice green and adjacent first tee area. And these are just the guys I recognize. Many more athletic-looking players that I don't know fill the field. It's hard not to notice the talent here—and even harder to focus in spite of it. All of them want this title as much as I do. Altogether, there are five groups of golfers, twenty players, with handicaps of 0 or better. Most have had experience in pressure-packed provincial and national men's tournaments. *This isn't junior golf anymore!*

The rest of the tournament field of 144 is made up of higher handicap divisions.

When Slinger's name is announced, a loud cheer erupts from the local fans. One guy yells, "Show 'em who's boss, Slinger." Kerry does not disappoint. He fires his drive down the left side of the fairway with a little fade, to the delight of the partisan crowd.

I suddenly feel intimidated. Am I the only player who's nervous out here? Everyone else appears so calm.

"Keep your mind on your business, Billy," Dad says calmly. "Don't worry about them. Take care of yourself. You'll be fine. You have as much talent as anyone here—and more than most."

I smile at Dad appreciatively. He doesn't smile back. He means what he said and I feel it. Dad's confidence in me makes me feel good about myself. So do Mom's and Danny's and Leah's. So do Tom's and Ben's. Dad's comments and Tom and Ben's messages have made all of the difference in the world to me right now, interrupting my destructive fearful thinking—the kind of thinking that paralyzes action and destroys performance. It's been a long time since I've stood near a first tee in any tournament feeling unsure if I would win—or even challenge.

Most of my nervousness has now subsided. My hands are dry. My legs are still. Why shouldn't I perform well? I've studied hard, worked hard and prepared well. My exercises have been going well. My swing and short game are as solid as they've ever been. I've prepared an outstanding strategy with which to approach the golf course—smart, yet aggressive. I've packed water and healthy snacks for energy. I'm organized. I'm ready. I'm confident.

Suddenly, I feel *eager* to start. Suddenly, the energy around the first tee becomes invigorating. I take a few deep breaths in through my nose and let them out through my mouth, bringing the breath consciously up into the back of my rib cage on the *in* breath and pushing the *out* breath out with my stomach. I look at Dad, feel the notes from Ben and Tom in my pocket, and refocus on my putting routine. Grip, alignment, balance, sequence—boom! The ball rolls firmly into the middle of the hole from six feet. And again. And again, rhythmically. Practice is over.

"I'm ready, Dad. Let's go."

Dad confidently corrals my putter from me and snatches up my golf bag. Side by side, we march to the first tee and meet the other players in the group, including John Nasland. What a thrill! I am sure to make respectful eye contact with each player. These guys are now my colleagues! I identify my golf ball and wish everyone good luck.

The previous group is out of sight down the first fairway.

This is it. The moment has arrived.

Lou Ogilvie is this year's Victoria Day starter. He saunters onto the first tee box, clipboard in hand. "Introducing the 10:30 tee time—teeing off first—from Calgary—John Nasland."

Nasland nods, acknowledging the respectful applause. His actions are silky smooth and rhythmic. Nasland effortlessly launches his ball down the right side of the fairway with a little *butter* draw. Perfect. Beautiful. The crowd applauds warmly for the legend.

As VanDerkadden and Alfman hit their drives, I focus on how the wind is affecting ball flight. Both hit decent drives. Both appear calm in their actions.

I am up. I am next. It is time to dare and dare again and go on daring.

Lou shuffles back onto the tee box and winks at me supportively.

"Now on the tee—" he bellows, with a crooked smile, "from Medicine Hat—Billy Black!"

The crowd explodes, sending my heart into a wild pound. I've never felt support like this before. I nod and smile in appreciation, feeling both shocked and energized.

Then, the strangest thing happens. My focus becomes acute—and time slows down. I easily channel my energy toward my pre-shot routine, becoming unaware of my surroundings, save for this shot at hand. The wind comes from behind and right, helping a draw. The par 5 first hole is reachable in two today with a good drive. I tee my ball high, step behind it and pick my target—a beautiful bushy, dark-green spruce tree in the distance. My target is all that exists. I move beside the ball rhythmically and aim my clubface down the target line. I take my grip. Position—good. Pressure—good. I align my body down the power line. Posture—connection—good. I waggle my club head to sense the motion to follow.

My pre-shot routine takes fourteen seconds. I've practiced it so many times that it's become automatic, second nature—providing a familiar flow and focal point under pressure. Dad, Gus, Tom and Ben have each stressed the importance of a consistent pre-shot routine.

My body feels relaxed and balanced. I am confident of my alignment. I'm ready to hit the shot. I let out a slow, rhythmic breath.

My swing motion seems to happen on its own, as if I am an observer. My upper body turns back against the resistance of my lower body, drawing the club back rhythmically. I turn until I can turn no more. My posture and balance are unyielding. My transition is controlled and solid. I instinctively drive my legs and hips down the power line, maintaining my spine angle, stable butt and chin position. My left hip clears easily. My arms are connected to my body. My hands remain passive. The club head is last to arrive at the ball, moving as one with the motion of my balanced body. I sense little of the contact with the ball, yet hear a hollow cracking. The ball catapults powerfully. My momentum brings me to a natural, balanced finish facing my target. I look up and spot my ball soaring down the fairway like a rocket. It feels perfect and powerful and natural! I hold my position, mesmerized by the dynamic bore of the ball's flight.

Suddenly, echoing silence gives way to thunderous applause as I once again become cognizant of my surroundings. The crowd noise sends another shot of adrenaline through my body. I've given them something to cheer about! I'm as happy for them as I am for myself!

The tee shot is over, yet my heart is still pounding wildly. Dad and I begin to walk together down the fairway enjoying the yells of encouragement. I again sense the presence of family, friends, girlfriend, coaches and gallery, all helping me through this unfamiliar moment. Never before has so much emotion moved through me. The energy numbs me.

Then it strikes me. What if the negative thoughts that I had been experiencing earlier hadn't been interrupted? How would my tee shot have turned out then? Dad, Ben and Tom had, in essence, hit that shot for me. Can I recreate that same mindset for each shot? I can't read new messages before every shot, can I? I can't be distracted from fear each swing, can I? This new level of golf will require a new level of mental knowledge, application and review, a new level of change and growth.

Most of the first tee crowd, including the cameraman and reporters, are following our group down the first fairway. Maybe they're following me, maybe John Nasland.

I overhear reporter Ted Sillinger ramble into his microphone: "Billy Black has just ripped his first drive down the middle of the fairway. He should be able to reach the par 5 first easily in two."

Dad rustles beside me, golf bag in tow. "Nice shot, kid," he says proudly, his walk in rhythm with mine.

"Thanks, Dad," I return excitedly, "I was lucky to have you and Tom and Ben around to refocus me."

Dad smiles. "Ben has one more message for you this weekend."

"Another note?" I ask anxiously.

"No, Billy. He wanted me to tell you to play hard and enjoy this experience. Keep your thoughts current and constructive. Commit to each shot. Do your best in each situation, no matter the degree—or lack of degree—of apparent challenge. Ben says your next focus together will be on the emotional and mental aspects of golf performance—no different than maximizing your performance in life, relationships, business, health, music, sales—anything. He says this study will fascinate you."

I suck in a forceful breath, nervously survey the large crowd following our group and chuckle dryly. "Trust me, Dad—I'm already fascinated."

The End

In Memory Of:

Richard Zachary, William Dooley, Mike Winther, Rick
Parkinson and Steve Winters

A final message ...

I hope you enjoyed the first installment of the story of Billy Black, as he commences his pursuit of success in golf and, unwittingly, life. Look for future volumes, as Billy's story offers continual insights in the pursuit of life's wisdoms and lower golf scores. Have you ever wondered what it takes to really "make it" as a professional golfer? How does one improve performance? You'll find out first hand, all based on the real life experiences of touring professionals and others. Much is ahead for Billy Black.

The game of golf relentlessly teaches us the importance of welcoming the messages hidden within *"failure and struggle"*. Rarely will any player, at any level, execute more than a handful of shots perfectly during a round of golf. Golf-shots are filled humorously with universal laws. Universal laws dictate outcomes without prejudice, despite the beliefs of any individual. The opportunity to learn is ever-present.

In a day when more and more role models depict success to their audience as personal gain at all cost, golf seduces its protégés much differently. Instead, like a caring parent, it accompanies young and old to observe values, effort, respect, humor and honesty. Short cuts lead to long frustrations. Stile points and beauty are discarded, in favor of guts and dedication. Social and political circles matter not once tee breaks ground. Entry to the game is becoming increasingly unguarded, thanks to the leadership of many forward thinking human beings, not the least of whom is Tiger Woods.

Golf is maturing to be a game for all. And rightly so.

See you again,

Dr. Terry Zachary

"We may turn to God when our foundations are shaking
only to discover it is God who is shaking them."
–Hebrew saying

"Experience, which destroys innocence,
also leads one back to it."
–James Baldwin